Our World and the Universe Around It

PART III | MATTER AND ENERGY

OUR WORLD

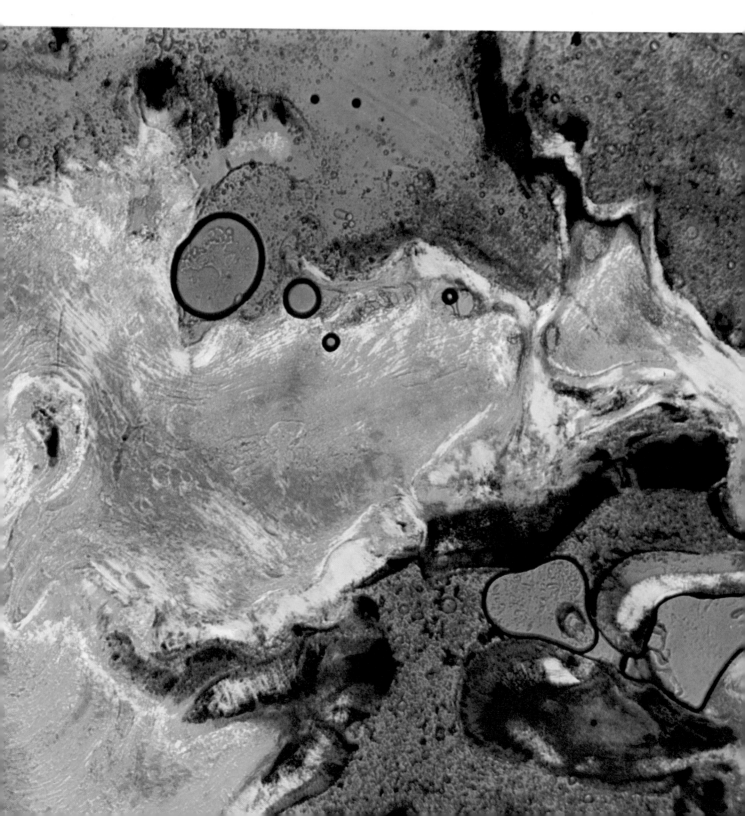

and the Universe Around It

PART III MATTER AND ENERGY

ORIGINAL TEXT IN ITALIAN BY Ginestra Amaldi

FREELY ADAPTED AND EXPANDED BY Norman Rudnick

PICTURE COMMENTARIES BY NORMAN RUDNICK

ABRADALE PRESS / Publishers / New York

Library of Congress Catalog Card Number: 66-12316

Designed by Howard Morris

PRINTED AND BOUND IN ITALY

Contents

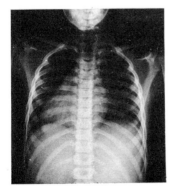

The Atomic Nucleus
and Its Elementary Particles

The atomic nucleus; Natural radioactivity; Alpha and beta rays; Gamma rays; The trail left by alpha, beta, and gamma rays; The cloud chamber; Cloud chamber snapshots of alpha-, beta-, and gamma-ray tracks; Realization of an old dream; The neutron; What an atomic nucleus is made of; A neutron gives birth to an electron; Nuclear forces and nuclear energy; Isotopes; Artificial radioactivity; A drop of liquid; The chain reaction and the uses of nuclear energy.

MATTER
AND ENERGY

Matter and Light

WE HAVE NOW RETURNED from imaginary journeys through space to the planets and stars, and through time to the early eras of the earth. We watched the procession of great events and the movements of massive bodies. These events and movements were on such a large scale that, for the most part, we were spectators at a distance. It was as if we were enjoying an imposing performance from a seat high in a grandstand. Now we will take a closer look at the things that fill our world.

MATTER

EVERYWHERE WE FIND what we call *matter*. It comes in three forms: solid, liquid, and gas. Jupiter is matter. Our bodies are matter. The land, the sea, and the air are mat-

263. The task of the physicist. *The chemical structure of the drug Hydrochlorothiazide is revealed in a photomicrograph. The structure, motion, and form of matter, sound, light, heat, and radiation, all are the objects of the physicist's investigation. He observes and experiments, trying to extract from his findings the laws that govern the world around him.*

ter. We will learn that there are forms of matter too small for us to see even with the finest microscope. An old definition states that matter is anything that occupies space. We will see that this definition has limited usefulness.

There are other things that are not matter. We cannot touch them, or taste them, or smell them. Some of these are light, heat, radio waves, x-rays, and the gamma rays that are emitted from radioactive materials like radium and uranium. We will learn that these are merely different forms of the same thing, electromagnetic radiation.

The Task of the Physicist The study of matter and radiation falls primarily in the field of physics. *Physics* is the science which deals with such ideas as sound, light, heat, electricity, and the structure of matter. It is concerned with the motion of objects as small as an electron or as big as a planet. It covers the changes in the form of matter, such as the evaporation of water from a liquid to a gas, or the melting of iron from a solid to a liquid. Physicists also investigate the behavior of radiation, whether from the bulb of a flashlight or the nucleus of a radium atom. As you can see from this range of interest, physics is probably the most fundamental of all natural sciences and overlaps all the others.

The physicist observes matter and radiation in all their bewildering forms, motions, and interactions. He sets himself the task of picking his way through the complex maze of things and events, weeding out misleading notions and selecting the significant facts. From these he tries to extract the laws which describe as simply as possible the things he has observed. If he is successful in finding a law which unravels the tangle of evidence he has gathered, he can also predict what will happen under different circumstances from those he has already witnessed.

Nature, however, is a jealous guardian of its laws. The detective work of the physicist is sometimes hard and often does not lead him to the final object of his investigation. However, the great patience required is often rewarded by the joy of discovery or, at the very least, the satisfaction that comes from exercising curiosity.

Science as we know it is not very old, compared with the long history of man. For thousands of years man tried to make sense out of his physical world. In his ignorant superstition, he first imagined that strange gods ordered people and objects about. Then man progressed to more intelligent observation and speculation about what he observed. Such observation and speculation reached a climax in ancient Greece, more than 300 years before Christ, when Aristotle compiled a great summary of scientific knowledge. His work was the supreme authority for about 2000 years. But what began as a scientific advance in ancient Greece gradually became a hindrance to scientific progress. We now know that Aristotle's philosophy was a mixture of fact and error, science and superstition. However, the influence of his writings was so great that very few dared to dispute his findings, even when the obvious evidence disagreed with them. Nevertheless, a beautiful but false theory is most easily destroyed by one or more stubborn facts that do not fit. It took 2000 years, but the stubborn facts finally accumulated. Modern science was born, aided by the insights of a few geniuses and by the gradual adoption of the *experimental method*.

The Experimental Method Until about 400 years ago, science was largely a listing of information gathered by men who observed the world around them as they found it. Men with clever minds sometimes tried to piece together some of the bits of information in order to find a pattern or law that organized the bits into some sensible scheme. We know now that such laws do exist and many have been discovered. However, these early scientists were faced with two great obstacles. They were misguided by incorrect theories inherited from Aristotle, and they were confused by an overabundance of detail that obscured the truly important facts.

264. Modern experimentation with specialized equipment. *This dry box built around a hydraulic press is used for compacting reactive powdered metals. Specialized equipment is an important factor in helping the modern scientist to plan, control, and operate his experiments.*

Here is an example of how the experimental method works. If a stone and a feather are dropped from a high window, they do not fall with the same speed. The stone plunges swiftly to the ground. The feather floats downward slowly, caught by any shift of wind (figure 265). If a man observes stones and feathers only as they happen to fall in everyday life, he will be likely to think only that light bodies fall slowly, and that heavy bodies fall swiftly. The zigzagging of the feather on the breezes only complicates matters. The important fact here is that the feather and the stone fall differently because there is air present. With no further information, our early sci-

265. Falling bodies in air. *When dropped together, a stone plunges straight down swiftly, but a feather falls more slowly, drifting about on the air. If the air were absent, the feather and the stone would fall with equal speed and strike the ground at the same time.*

entist could not arrive at the single law which governs the falling of all bodies, light or heavy.

It is the essence of the experimental method that the experimenter does not accept only the facts that are presented to him by chance. Instead, he tests various ideas by arranging conditions to suit himself. In this way he can eliminate many of the confusing details that are not of primary interest. He can also remove influences that hide the simple, underlying relationships. For example, in the case of the stone and the feather, he might suspect that the presence of air makes it harder to understand how things fall. He can then arrange to drop the stone and the feather in a vacuum —say, in a long tube from which he has

pumped the air. He then finds that they fall with equal speed and strike the bottom of the tube together. He learns this surprising and revealing fact from an experimental situation which he can never find in nature.

Galileo and the Motion of Falling Objects

The greatest of the first experimenters was Galileo Galilei (figure 266), who lived from 1564 to 1642. The experimental method, which seems simple enough to us now, was revolutionary in Galileo's time. The respect for Aristotle's philosophy had been a habit for so long that it had hardened into resistance to any opposing ideas. Since almost everything anyone might want to know could be found in Aristotle, why look further? The religious mood of the age also discouraged scientific questioning, except along orthodox lines. To do otherwise was to go against God.

Galileo made great strides in modern experimental science by observing and defining the simple laws obeyed by falling objects. Time after time, he dropped weights of different shapes and sizes from the Leaning Tower of Pisa and studied their fall. He recognized the effect of the air on the fall of feathers and other light objects. Heavy objects fell straight and true, but so fast that measurements were difficult. To avoid this difficulty, he did what few others had done before him: he designed experiments.

Galileo rolled balls down sloping surfaces and controlled the speed of the balls by tilting the surface at various angles. A ball rolling down a slope is really falling straight down and moving sideways at the same time. The part of the motion that consists of falling straight down—that is, from one height to a lower height—is very similar to the motion of a ball falling freely from a tower. The action is merely slowed down. The rolling ball does encounter friction with the surface it rolls on. To minimize this, Galileo made the balls smooth, hard, and round, and covered the surface of his sloping plane with thin parchment.

The slowing of the motion of the falling balls permitted Galileo to discover the simple laws obeyed by all bodies falling in empty space. His results were accurate in spite of the fact that his experiments were performed in air and not a vacuum. This is because the resistance of air to the motion of an object passing through it is less if the object is moving slowly, more if the object is moving rapidly. When the object is moving fast, it compresses the air in front of it before the air has a chance to move aside. Since the particles of air are then bunched more closely together, the air is denser and offers greater resistance. The balls in Galileo's experiments were smooth and round, and moving slowly enough so that the presence of the air had only a very small effect.

What Galileo found is that all bodies falling freely in empty space fall at the same speed regardless of weight. He also found that the speed does not remain the same, but increases constantly as the body falls. The speed increases in proportion to the length of time the body has been falling. This means that the speed attained after 2 seconds is twice that reached in only 1

second. After 4 seconds of fall, the body is traveling 4 times as fast as after the first second, and so on, until the ground interrupts the fall. From such experiments as Galileo's, modern science was born.

Meanwhile, Johannes Kepler, who lived from 1571 to 1630, was also observing falling bodies, although he did not recognize them as such. Kepler's falling bodies were the planets. Just as Galileo's hard spheres

266. Galileo Galilei (1564–1642). *Galileo is regarded as the father of modern physics not so much because of his great discoveries, but because he demonstrated the importance of using experiments to obtain information and to test theories. His work on falling objects proved Aristotle wrong and laid the basis for further developments by Newton.*

267. Johannes Kepler (1571–1630). *Kepler was a great German astronomer who passionately sought to find order in the heavens. He discovered three important laws of planetary motion which were later explained by Sir Isaac Newton on the basis of gravitational forces.*

in their path down the tilted boards were falling toward the earth and moving sideways at the same time, so the planets are falling toward the sun and also veering off to one side. Because they move sideways rapidly enough as they approach the sun, the planets always manage to fall clear of the sun without hitting it. The situation is something like the sport in which you use a little wooden paddle to hit a rubber ball that is attached to the paddle by a long rubber band. After being hit, the ball races away, stretching the elastic band. The stretched rubber pulls the ball back toward the paddle, just as the sun pulls the planets toward itself. The little ball returns toward the paddle. In a sense, it is falling into the paddle, but it also picks up motion sideways or up or down. If this motion off to one side is great enough, the ball misses the paddle completely.

Kepler found three laws governing planetary motion. These laws were somewhat like Galileo's laws, but more complicated. At a time when most people still believed that the sun and the planets moved around the earth, Kepler found that the earth and the other planets really moved around the sun. This agreed with Copernicus, who had suggested this idea before Kepler. Kepler also found that the paths of the planets were elliptical orbits with the sun at one focus of all the ellipses. Since the orbits are not perfect circles, a planet is not always the same distance from the sun. Sometimes it is closer to and sometimes it is farther from the sun.

The description of the orbits of the planets around the sun is Kepler's *first law*. Kepler's other laws must have been considered only mathematical curiosities at the time. However, their true significance became apparent not too long afterward.

The *second law* concerned the peculiar action of an imaginary line drawn between a planet and the sun. Imagine, if you can, that this line is an enormous, elastic garden hose, perforated with little holes and spraying water along its full length. The space between the planet and the sun is a great, cosmic lawn. As the planet swings around the sun, the imaginary hose has to shrink and stretch because the planet is nearer the sun in some parts of its orbit and more distant in others. In this strange situation, Kepler discovered that the amount of lawn watered during any given period of time is always the same, regardless of which part of the ellipse the planet is in during that time. This situation requires that the planet move fastest when the garden hose is shortest—that is, when the planet is nearest the sun. The planet must speed up because a shorter hose must go faster to cover the same amount of lawn in the given time. When the planet is farther from the sun and the hose is longer, the planet slows down.

Kepler stated his second law in this way: A line between the sun and a planet sweeps over equal areas in equal intervals of time.

The *third law* is the strangest. It deals with the *period* of a planetary orbit. Period is the name given to the length of time it takes a planet to complete its orbit once. Kepler's third law states that the square of the period (the period multiplied by itself) is proportional to the cube of the average distance of the planet from the sun (the distance multiplied by itself and then by itself again).

The mysteries were cleared up about 50 years later in 1665 by Sir Isaac Newton (figure 270) in one of the grandest scientific achievements ever made. In his *laws of motion* and of *gravitation* (the attraction of objects for each other), Newton summed up all the laws of Galileo and Kepler. Along with this accomplishment, Newton invented a kind of mathematics, called *calculus,* that made it possible to calculate exactly all sorts of complicated motions of bodies. These included the motions of any bodies, however large or small, whether on earth or in the heavens, so long as the forces acting on the bodies were known.

Why Apples Fall and Tides Come In   If the legend were true that an apple fell on Newton's head and jarred loose the idea of gravity, then we should all wish that more apples fall on more heads.

Newton stated all the fundamental facts about the motions of bodies in three laws. The *first law* says that a body will continue at rest or will maintain a constant speed in a straight line unless a force acts on it. A

268. Kepler's diagram showing the orbits of the planets. *In 1596 Kepler published his views on the solar system, winning recognition from Galileo and other eminent astronomers of his time.*

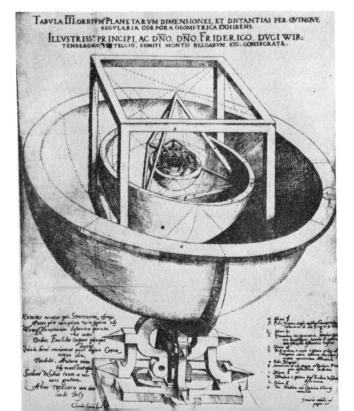

297

269. Force and velocity in flight. *This airplane model in vertical take-off illustrates Newton's laws in action. Opposition of air to being thrust downward by the propellers creates an upward force greater than that of gravity. Thus, the aircraft is accelerated upward, achieving a vertical velocity. At this point, the wings and propellers rotate position, so that the propelling force becomes horizontal. This produces a forward acceleration against the force of air resistance, while the air passing across the wing sustains the lift against gravity.*

condition of rest is really a constant speed of zero. At first glance, this law does not seem true. We know that a ball thrown up into the air rises first, makes an arc, and then falls back to earth. It certainly does not travel a straight line. Even a bullet from a gun does not fly straight, but eventually curves down toward the earth. In fact, nothing seems to move in a perfectly straight line. The answer, of course, is that all the objects we see are acted upon by forces that do change the motion from a straight line into a curve. The earth pulls all objects toward itself. The air pushes back against the ball and the bullet.

Newton saw the same curving motion that everyone else saw, but he extracted from this the underlying truth: that ever-present forces cause the curvature. He was able to imagine the absence of such forces and to appreciate what would happen in such an imaginary situation.

Before considering Newton's second law, let us be sure of the meanings of the words describing motion. In everyday conversation, the words "speed" and "velocity" are used as if they mean the same thing. In physics they serve different purposes. *Speed* denotes how fast an object is changing position, say in feet per second or miles per hour. *Velocity* indicates not only how fast, but also the direction in which a body is moving. Speed carries only one piece of information, velocity carries two.

Here is an example of the difference between speed and velocity. Two locomotives are one mile apart. They are traveling on the same track at the same speed. If their velocities are also the same, they are going in the same direction. Since their speeds are equal, the one behind never catches up to the one in front. If their velocities are opposite, although their speeds are the same, they are traveling toward each other and will soon collide. The difference between speed and velocity is therefore important to the engineers driving them.

A change in velocity can be a change in speed alone, a change in direction alone, or

298

a change in both. If we give an automobile more gasoline on a straight road, we change speed without changing direction. If we apply the brake to turn a corner, we change speed and direction together. If we drive around a circular track with a constant motion, we change direction continuously without changing speed. In all three cases, we change velocity and this requires the application of a force. The rate of change of velocity with time is called *acceleration,* whether the speed rises or falls or whether the change is in direction only.

The first law can now be restated more simply in our new terms. A body has a constant velocity (zero if at rest, a constant speed in a straight line if moving) unless acted on by a force. What we mean by a *force,* then, is something capable of changing the velocity of an object. In our new language, a force produces an acceleration.

Newton's *second law* says that the ac-celeration produced is directly proportional to the force producing it. If the force is doubled, the acceleration is doubled: the velocity changes twice as fast. *Inertia* is the name of the property of an object that resists a change in motion. Because a body has inertia, we must apply a force to change its motion. Heavy bodies have more inertia than light bodies. It is harder to change the motion of a heavy body, or to start it moving from a state of rest, than it is for a light body. *Mass* is the name given to describe the amount of inertia possessed by a body. Therefore, we can think of mass as being something like heaviness. It is related to weight, but it is not the same thing. The difference will be discussed later.

Newton's second law can also be expressed as an equation

$$f = ma$$

which says that the force f equals the mass m times the acceleration a produced when force f is applied to a body having mass m. Remember that acceleration means change of velocity. This means that as long as a force is applied to a body and it is accelerated because of the force, its velocity cannot settle down to a constant speed or direction. The body must always be speeding up, slowing down, or turning.

Recall that Galileo discovered that a falling ball increases in speed as it falls toward the ground. It undergoes acceleration. Therefore, it must be acted upon by a force. This force is the gravitational attraction of the earth, which we will examine again a little later.

Newton's first two laws explain why you can coast when riding a bicycle. You pedal hard to pick up speed. During this time you are applying force with your legs, partly to overcome friction in the axles, but mostly to change the velocity of the bicycle—that is, to accelerate it. But once you have reached the desired speed, you can stop pedaling, even though you are on level ground, and the bicycle will continue at that speed. A small amount of friction acts as a backward force against the speed of the bike and slows it down a little, but not much if the parts are well oiled. Newton's first law says that the bicycle will maintain a constant velocity by itself, without the help of additional force. You have to apply a force only to change the velocity. You pedal hard again if you want to gain more speed, press on the brake if you want to slow down, and apply force to the handle bars if you

want to change direction. Newton's second law describes how much force you must exert to achieve a particular change in the velocity.

Newton's *third law* states that every action has an equal and opposite reaction. *Action* usually refers to a force. Some examples will make this clearer. When you press your hand on a table, nothing moves, even though your hand may become tired. This is because the table top pushes up just as hard as you push down. But the table top does not push up until you push down. Therefore your push is the action and that of the table top is the *reaction*. The forces are equal in size but opposite in direction. They cancel each other and there is no motion. It is as though there were no force at all.

When the fuel in a rocket ship burns, it produces gases that expand and rush out the tail opening. The ship speeds forward, but not because the gases are pushing against air. At high altitudes there is practically no air. The force thrusting the rocket ship forward is the reaction to the force blasting the gases backward.

Thus, the reaction need not be a stationary force. When you push a stalled car off the road, the car moves, but you are very much aware that something is pushing back at you. Your push is the action. The reaction is made up partly of friction between moving parts in the car, and partly of the acceleration of the mass of the car. The mass times acceleration, ma in the equation $f=ma$, is the amount of the latter part of the reaction. There is also some small reaction from the air which must be displaced to let the car through.

With Newton's laws and the mathematics he developed, almost all motions can be predicted forever if we know the velocity at any one time and the forces that are acting. What are the forces that drive the planets to obey Kepler's strange laws?

Newton alone saw the resemblance between the planets and Galileo's falling spheres. He showed that the laws of Galileo and Kepler followed automatically if he assumed that the forces causing planets and apples to move as they do came from an attraction between bodies of matter. Newton developed the Law of Universal Gravitation which applies to all matter, all bodies, everywhere.

The law of gravitation states that any two pieces of matter attract each other with a certain force. The strength of this force is greater if the masses of the two bodies are greater and if the two bodies are closer together. The exact relationship is

$$f = G \frac{m_1 \times m_2}{r^2}$$

where f is the force pulling one body to the other, m_1 and m_2 are the masses of the bodies, r is the distance between the two bodies (between their centers if they are big compared with the distance between them), and G is a number called the *gravitational constant*. The actual number that G assumes depends on whether the mass and distance are expressed in grams and centimeters, pounds and feet, or tons and miles. Whatever G is for a given choice of units, it is the same for all matter everywhere. r^2 is merely the distance r multiplied by itself. To find the force between two marbles or between a planet and the sun, we have only to multiply the two masses together, multiply the result by G, and divide this result by the square of the distance between the two objects.

Now we know why we stick to the surface

270. Sir Isaac Newton (1642–1727). *His superb mind produced advances in so many branches of science, that Newton, of all the scientists of the past, was probably the greatest single contributor to knowledge. Among his grandest achievements were the laws of motion and the Law of Universal Gravitation from which the paths of planetary orbits could be predicted.*

of the earth. There is a gravitational attraction between our bodies and the earth which draws us together. The force depends on the product of our own mass and the mass of the earth and this force is what we call our weight. Although the gravitational pull of the earth is an ordinary example of an attraction between masses, it is given a special name. It is called *gravity*.

It may seem queer, but the earth is attracted to us by the same force which attracts us to the earth. If a man jumps into the air to separate himself from the earth, he and the earth come right back together again. Does his body in the air pull the earth up to him, or does the earth pull his body down to it? The answer to both questions is yes, but there is a big difference. The force on the earth and the force on the man may be the same, but the mass of the earth is one hundred thousand billion billion times the mass of the man. When the same force acts on both, it accelerates the man's body one hundred thousand billion billion times more than it accelerates the earth. It seems safe to say that the man is pulled back to earth.

We have now arrived at the difference between weight and mass. The mass of a body determines how much it will be accelerated by a particular force, according to the equation $f = ma$. The *weight* of a body is the force exerted on it by the attraction of the earth or other planet on which it sits. Therefore, weight is not mass, it is force. It is the force calculated from the equation for the gravitational attraction between two bodies. This force depends on the mass of both attracting bodies, not on one alone.

On another planet, the mass would be the same as on earth. A given force would accelerate a body to the same extent on another planet as on earth. However, the weight would be different. The weight would be the force with which the body is pulled toward that planet. This depends not only on the mass of the body but also on the mass of the planet. Thus, mass is a property of a body that is the same everywhere. Weight is a force of attraction between a body and the particular planet it happens to visit.

In fact, a way to reduce weight painlessly is to go to Mars. Your mass would remain the same, but the mass of Mars is only one-ninth that of the earth. Mars is smaller than the earth, however. Since you would be closer to the center of Mars than you are to the center of the earth, the attraction between you would tend to be greater. The result is that your weight is reduced not to one-ninth of your weight on earth, but only to just under one-half of your earth weight. If you weigh about 200 pounds on earth and can hardly walk upstairs, on Mars you would weigh 100 pounds and could be a high jumper.

When Newton applied his laws of gravitation and motion to the masses of the sun and the planets, he found that their predicted paths agreed exactly with Kepler's laws. The sun is like a boy swinging a rock about him on the end of a string. The rock is like a planet. The force in the string keeps the rock at a certain distance from the boy and prevents the rock from flying off at a tangent as it would do the instant the string were cut. Between the sun and a planet, the force in the string is replaced by the force of gravitation. The force of gravitation is like a string made of rubber. If the boy had a rubber string that could become longer or shorter, he would find that the string became longer when he swung the rock faster, shorter when he swung the rock more slowly. In a similar way, the distance between the sun and a planet bears a definite relation to the speed with which the planet revolves about the sun.

Why do apples fall? Because they are attracted to the earth by gravity. Why do tides come in? Because the moon attracts the earth and loose matter like water moves toward the moon, whereas solid matter tends to remain behind. Newton truly captured the harmony of the universe in his laws.

LIGHT

Light, Waves, and Color   Now we turn to things in the universe that do not consist of matter. The most familiar to us is light. Light brings messages from other worlds. It scatters the shadows and fills our lives with color. Light from the sun nourishes plants and animals. Light is vital to our existence, yet it is such a casual comfort that only the blind have a true awareness of its value.

What do we know of light? Experimental scientists worked with light for hundreds of years and put it to good use before there

271. Sir Isaac Newton experimenting with light rays. *Newton's genius applied to studies in optics advanced our understanding of the behavior of light and the phenomenon of color.*

was even a glimmer of understanding of its nature. Modern theoretical scientists have come closer to an understanding of light, but our knowledge today is still far from complete. Before talking of what it is, let us first discuss what light does.

A beam of light travels in a straight line until it meets an obstacle. When the beam passes from air to glass, from glass to water, or between any two unlike materials, the beam bends. It travels along a new straight line in the new medium. This is called *refraction*. Light seems to bounce from light-

303

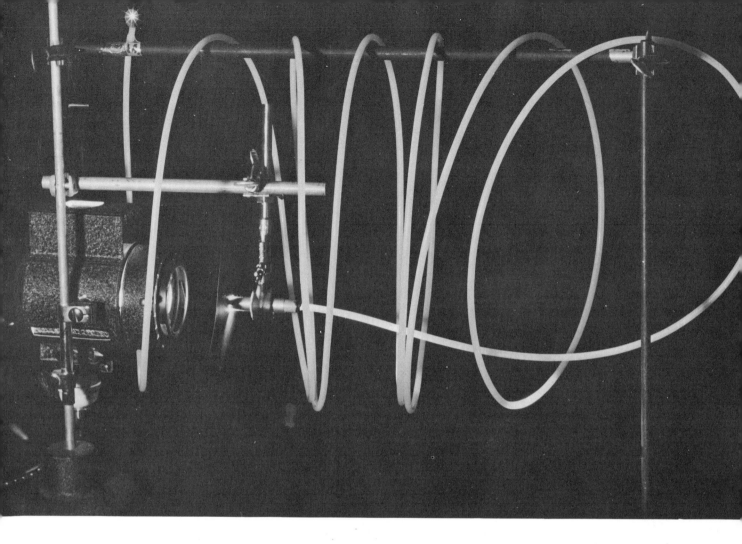

272. Light pipe. *Light from the lamp enters the "pipe" (left center), travels over 20 feet around curves, and emerges as a bright spot (upper left). The pipe is a bundle of very fine glass fibers, each thinly coated with a second type of glass. A light ray entering a fiber under the proper conditions becomes trapped and proceeds down the fiber, reflecting from side to side in a zigzag path.*

colored or shiny surfaces like mirrors. This is called *reflection*. The angles through which the light bends by refraction or reflection follow certain simple mathematical laws. By curving glass and mirror surfaces in accordance with these laws, scientists have performed remarkable tricks with light. They have constructed telescopes and microscopes, eyeglasses, spectroscopes, movie projectors, cameras, and many other useful or entertaining devices.

In empty space light races at the amazing speed of 186,000 miles a second. In air it is only slightly less. In water or glass, the light travels more slowly, but still at phenomenal speeds. The angle of refraction mentioned above depends on the difference between the speeds of light in the two materials between which light passes. If sunshine is narrowed by a slit into a thin ribbon of light and passed through a *prism* (a triangular bar of glass), the ribbon fans out into a rainbow spray of colors. The reason for this is that each color of light travels at a different speed in the glass. Therefore, each color bends through a different angle and the colors become separated.

Many other fascinating facts about light were discovered. Men used these facts as clues to the answer to the question: What is light? Their guesses followed two opposing lines of thought. One group suggested that a beam of light was really a flight of tiny particles, or corpuscles. This was called the *corpuscular theory*. According to this theory, color is related to the size of the particles. The other theory claimed that light had the form of waves traveling through space. This was called the *wave theory*. To understand what we mean by a wave, let us consider some more familiar waves, the ripples caused by a stone dropping into water.

When a stone is dropped into a pond which has a still, glassy surface, little rings form and spread outward in larger and larger circles. If we examine a snapshot of the rippled surface we find two kinds of rings. One kind has dipped below the normal surface level like a circular ditch scooped out of the water. The other kind of ring stands up above the normal surface level. The two kinds of rings follow each other in a regular sequence, first a low ring, then a high ring, then a low, then a high, and so on. This succession of highs and lows is called a *wave*. The wave is said to move because the point where there is now a low ring soon develops a high ring. A point where there is now a high ring soon develops a low ring. To the eye it looks as if each ring, low and high alike, has moved outward one position to replace the ring it follows. Actually, the water does not move outward at all. It merely remains in place, rising or falling depending on the part of the wave that is passing a given point at a

given time. A cork set afloat on the water will not drift outward with the wave. It will bob up and down in one place. We say that the disturbance caused by the stone is moving through the water.

The wave is described by three characteristics: velocity, wave length, and frequency. The *velocity* is the rate at which a given ring appears to move away from the center where the stone dropped. The *wave*

273. Fibers in a light pipe. *These glass fibers, seen end on, are only 80 millionths of an inch thick. The bright fibers are transmitting light directly. Patterns surrounding them are caused by interference of light leaked to neighboring fibers. A bundle of such fibers can transmit a picture over 100 feet around corners, each fiber carrying a tiny portion of the image.*

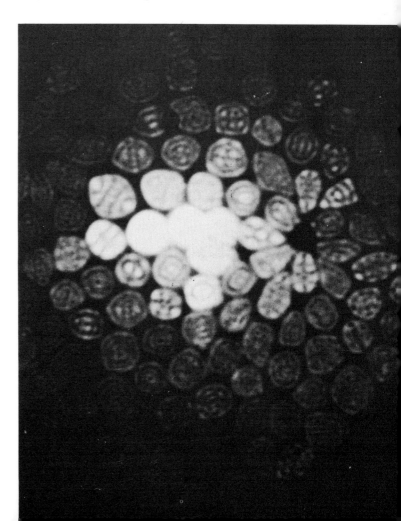

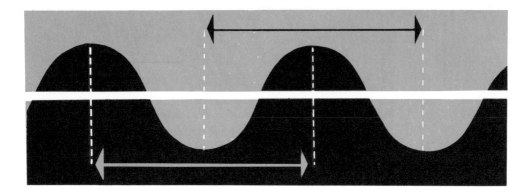

274. Wave motion. *Waves are described by three numbers: Wave length—the distance from one peak to the next (or trough to trough); Velocity—the speed with which a point on the wave travels from place to place; and Frequency—the number of waves that pass a given point in one second. The numbers are related by the equation: Velocity = Frequency × Wave length.*

length is the distance from the center of a low ring to the center of the next low ring. This is the same as from high ring to high ring, as shown in figure 274. *Frequency* is the number of low rings (or high rings) that pass a given point during a unit time interval.

We can think of frequency in another way. If we watch the water at a given point on its surface, say the top of a high region in figure 275, we see the water fall and then rise again. When it rises as high as it will go, it starts the same motion all over again. This part of the motion, from high point to low point and back to high point, is called a *cycle*. The motion of the wave is just a repetition of these cycles at every point on the surface of the water. The frequency is the number of times this cycle occurs at one place during a unit time. If the unit is a second, we express the frequency in cycles per second. If the unit is a minute, we say cycles per minute, and so on.

What have the ripples in a pond to do with light? The supporters of the wave theory of light said that light was just such a wave traveling through space. At each point along the path of the light something was changing, just the way the surface of the water bobbed up and down. It was not known what was changing, whether it was motion of some substance or merely varia-

275. Waves in water. *Ripples radiating from a point of disturbance are evidence of the passage of waves through the water. Energy transmitted to the pond by a falling pebble travels outward in rings of high pressure followed by rings of low pressure.*

tions in some property of the region the light crossed. As a wave, light had the three characteristics. Its velocity was 186,000 miles per second. Its wave length could be measured by ingenious experiments which also resulted in measurements of frequency.

The arguments for the two different theories of light raged back and forth. Then a remarkable discovery was made, apparently deciding the dispute for all time in favor of the wave theory.

Waves Discovered on Paper During the first half of the nineteenth century, Michael Faraday performed brilliant research into the nature of electricity and magnetism. He discovered that there is a relation between the two. Bits of electricity are called *charges* and are of two different kinds, called *plus* and *minus*. Plus charges push away other plus charges and minus charges push away other minus charges, but plus and minus charges attract each other. Magnets do not come in bits. Rather they must always have length, with opposite ends that differ from each other somewhat the way plus charges differ from minus charges. One end of a magnet is called the *north pole* and the other the *south pole*. The north poles of two magnets repel each other and the south poles of two magnets repel each other, but the south pole of one attracts the north pole of the other. In both electricity and magnetism, likes repel and unlikes attract.

If there were no motion of charges and poles and no change in the amount of electricity and magnetism, the electric charges and the magnets would have no effect on each other. However, this is not the usual state of affairs.

Michael Faraday discovered that a moving magnet can produce electricity and moving electric charges can produce magnetism. His discovery led to such useful devices as the generator in a modern automobile in which a coil of wire is rotated

276. Michael Faraday (1791–1867). *Faraday was not only a gifted scientist who made important contributions in the fields of physics and chemistry, but was also a talented inventor. His experiments with the interrelations between electricity and magnetism led to practical devices such as motors and generators.*

past a magnet to cause electricity to flow in the wire. This lights the headlamps, operates the radio and cigarette lighter, and charges the battery. The process by which the moving magnets and moving electric charges influence each other is called *electromagnetic induction*. It is not necessary for magnets and charges really to move from place to place. It is necessary only that the magnetic and electrical quantities be changing.

It has since been discovered that electricity and magnetism are frequently found mixed together. In fact, the magnetic properties of materials can be explained in terms of the spinning of tiny electric charges within the atoms of the material.

When an English mathematician and physicist by the name of James Clerk Maxwell was trying to express the findings of Faraday and others in mathematical form, he arrived at a group of four famous equations. In studying the equations, he found that under special conditions electricity flowing in a wire would somehow radiate waves out into space. These waves were something new. We saw how waves passing through water cause the surface of the water to rise and fall. In Maxwell's waves, it was the electrical and magnetic properties of the space around the wire that rose and fell. When the wave passes a given point, it should make itself felt as a magnetic and electrical influence at the same time, according to Maxwell's equations. For this reason they were called *electromagnetic waves*. Moreover, the equations permitted Maxwell to calculate how fast these mysteri-

308

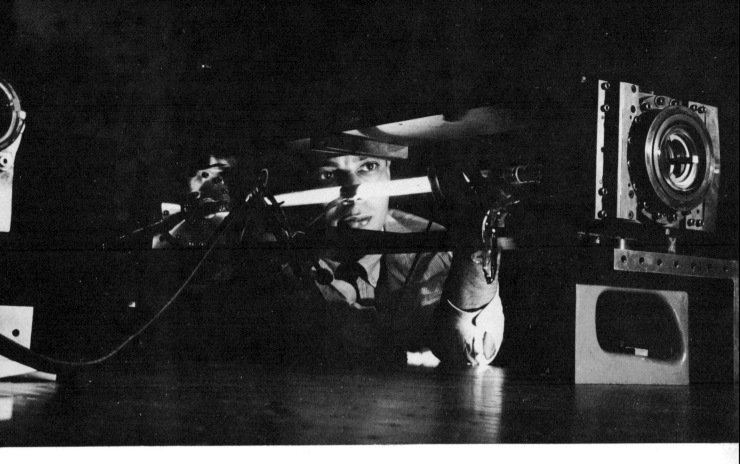

277. The gas laser. *An intense, narrow beam of light of remarkable properties is emitted by a tube containing a mixture of neon and helium gases controlled by a newly developed method. The device is a laser, named for Light Amplification by Stimulated Emission of Radiation. Laser light, also produced by certain crystals, such as ruby, is exceptionally pure in wave length (color) and does not weaken rapidly by diverging as do ordinary light beams. Of great potential value, laser beams can be flashed to the moon or focused to melt the most resistant material.*

ous waves should travel. Their speed proved to be 186,000 miles per second, exactly the speed of light.

About 1885, 6 years after Maxwell died, his waves discovered on paper were actually produced with an electrical circuit by Heinrich Rudolph Hertz. These waves were very similar to the radio waves we use for broadcasting. In fact, in Europe these are sometimes known as *Hertzian waves.* Usually, we describe the frequency of radio waves in *kilocycles,* each kilocycle representing 1000 cycles per second. In honor of Hertz, kilocycles are sometimes called *kilohertz.*

It was natural that the supporters of the wave theory of light should try to fit Max-

well's electromagnetic waves into their theories. They fitted very well. The wave theory of light became universally accepted and light was considered to be an electromagnetic wave.

In this theory, the color of light depends on the frequency of the wave, just as the note emitted by a piano depends on the frequency of vibration of the string which is struck. White sunlight is similar to a musical chord in which several piano keys are struck at once, the different frequencies blending together. The rainbow is the spread of frequencies of light that our eyes can detect. Red is at the low-frequency end and violet at the high-frequency end.

But light is only a small part of the range of electromagnetic waves. It is a special part only because our eyes happen to be able to see waves with frequencies between red and violet. The electromagnetic waves with frequencies below red and above violet are quite similar to light, but we cannot see them. We must use other instruments to detect them. Below the frequency of red light there is infrared light which is invisible but carries heat. Below the infrared are the many radio frequencies used for broadcasting, television, and communications. Above the frequency of violet light is ultraviolet light. It is the ultraviolet light in sunshine which is largely responsible for sunburn, even though it is light we cannot see. Above the ultraviolet there are x-rays, gamma rays, and other rays, some of which have been discovered only recently by nuclear physicists.

Once light appeared to be firmly established as a wave, there still remained a very difficult problem. To scientists in the late nineteenth century, all waves needed some substance to carry them along. It was understandable that waves like sound could pass through water, air, or solid material. The sound vibrated some particles of the water, the air, or the solid material. These, in turn, bumped the next particles and so on, passing the wave along like runners in a relay race passing a stick from runner to runner. What substance carried the light waves from the sun? Was there some invisible matter between the earth and the sun? Sound waves would not travel through a vacuum. Therefore, it was as-

sumed that light waves could not do so either.

Since there was no known substance that met the requirements, one was invented. It was called the *ether*. This was not the ether that puts us to sleep before a surgical operation. It was a mysterious form of matter that was assumed to fill all space throughout the universe. It had the necessary properties to pass light waves and yet did not interfere with the motion of planets. It was assumed to be thinner than air. Many experiments failed to detect the ether and fantastic theories explained the failures. Then, early in the twentieth century, Albert Michelson and Edward Morley performed an experiment with equipment so sensitive and precise that their results could not be doubted. The ether did not exist. Scientists had to accept the fact that light could pass through empty space. It was also found that the speed of light is constant regardless of the speed of the source.

Waves and Particles We conclude the discussion of light with the strangest paradox of all. After all the successful research that proved that light behaved like a wave, modern physics has found that light can also act like a stream of particles. In some

278. Light and matter. *Under ultraviolet light, cadmium sulfide crystals fluoresce brilliantly. Green indicates a pure crystal; yellow and red denote impurities. In fluorescence, an ultraviolet ray is absorbed. It is high in energy, short in wave length, and therefore invisible. The crystal releases this absorbed energy in several rays. Since the emitted rays have lower energy, they also have longer wave lengths and are visible as colored light.*

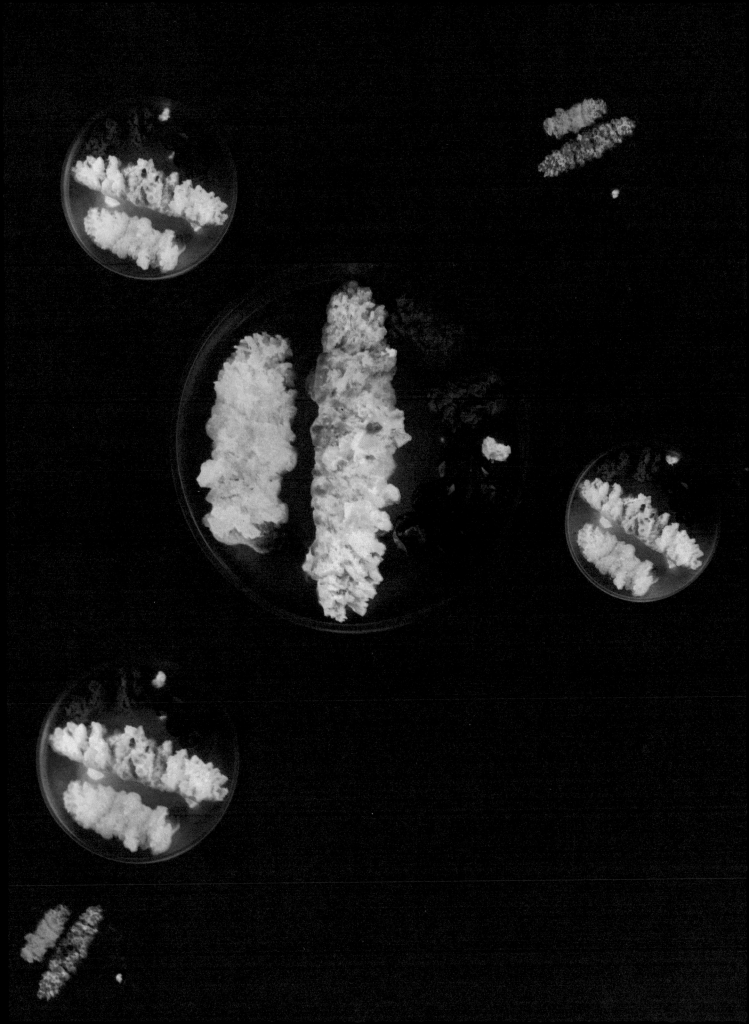

279. Albert Einstein (1879–1955). *Einstein was best known for his Theory of Relativity which described, among other things, the equivalence of mass and energy and the effect of gravitation on light. The Nobel Prize in 1921 honored him for other major contributions to physics as well, such as his explanation of the photoelectric effect and the nature of specific heats.*

strange way, all electromagnetic waves are both waves and particles. If you use instruments that detect waves, you find waves. If you use instruments that detect particles, you find particles. It has also been found that all forms of matter have this double nature. They are both waves and particles. It is even possible to calculate what happens when light collides with a particle of matter. To a large extent, this can be treated as a collision between two tiny billiard balls.

Nothing Can Run Faster than Light But how can matter be electromagnetic waves when matter moves so slowly and electromagnetic waves dash along at 186,000 miles a second? The answer is somewhat complicated. A particle of matter is not a simple wave of only one frequency. It is a package of waves of many frequencies which mix and interfere with each other. They interfere in such a way that in one region they add to and support each other, and everywhere else they subtract from and cancel each other. Here is a simple example of how waves can do this.

Imagine that two stones are dropped into a pool of water at some distance from each other. Two separate sets of ripples spread out from the two separate centers. Soon the ripples from one stone will cut across the ripples from the other stone. Let us find a point where the wave from one stone tries to form a dip in the water below the normal level, and where the wave from the second stone is trying to raise a high ring above the normal level. The two waves are trying to do opposite things to the water at this point. As a result the water stands still and neither rises nor falls at this point. This is called *destructive interference*. At another point the two waves may both be trying to raise the water. Here the water will rise twice as high, but as if only one wave were present. This is called *constructive interference*.

Therefore, a particle of matter can be a group of electromagnetic waves that mix in constructive interference in the region where we see the particle. They mix destructively—that is, cancel each other—in all other places.

When matter moves slowly, the waves do not move slowly. Rather the place where they add to each other moves slowly while the waves themselves race along as usual.

When matter moves very rapidly surprising things happen, as predicted by the *theory of relativity* of Albert Einstein. Based, in part, on the constancy of the speed of light, this theory declares that matter actually becomes heavier when it moves faster. The increase in mass is extremely small for ordinary speeds so we cannot even measure it. However, when the speeds approach the speed of light, the mass begins to increase enormously. If a body could actually reach the speed of light, its mass would increase to infinity. Since this is not possible, Einstein really demonstrated that the speed of light is the fastest speed that any bit of matter can ever reach. It cannot really reach this speed, it can only come close.

We have now concluded our discussion about what makes up the things in the universe and how they move. There is matter and there are electromagnetic waves, of which light is a small part. In view of the discoveries of recent years, we are not even sure that matter and light are really two different ideas. They now appear to be two members of the same group, two different aspects of waves. However, the present condition of scientific knowledge is so complicated that, wherever possible, we go back to older ways of thinking. For example, as long as Newton's equations provide an accurate picture of the motion of baseballs, automobiles, and artillery shells, we use Newton's equations, not Einstein's. For the fast, tiny particles in atoms, Newton's equations do not give the right answers, so we use the equations of Einstein and other modern physicists.

Now we will turn from the subject of how matter moves to the details of how matter is constructed and how matter is transformed from one kind to another.

Substances and Molecules

NATURE PRESENTS US with a magnificent variety of substances. Even within the small part of the world which is our room, the number of different substances is great. There are the ceramic in the lamp; the glass in the light bulbs and windows; the wood in the desk, chairs, and walls; the paper in pads and books and cartons; the cloth fabrics in bedsheets, chair coverings, clothing, curtains, and bookbindings; the leather, rubber, and steel in our shoes; the linoleum under the rug; the gold in a watch and a ring; and the air we breathe. We have listed only a fraction of the substances in our small room and yet this is but the minutest part of all the substances in nature. If we glance out our window, the range is magnified enormously. We see many forms of wood, water, iron, stone (figure 280), and other substances stretching out to the horizon.

Some of the substances seem ageless, like the glass in the windows, the concrete pavements on the street, a large stone in the meadow, or the bricks in the wall of the house. Others we expect to age slowly, like the steel bodies of passing automobiles, the fallen tree in the woods, the aluminum pans in the kitchen, the doors, cabinets, and wooden furniture. Still other substances have only fleeting existences, like perishable foods, delicate flowers, gasoline that burns in a flash or evaporates quickly when spilled, match heads that flare up and are suddenly gone, and other violently active chemicals that fume, corrode, or explode.

All of these substances have two things in common. They are all forms of matter, and they are all changing from one form to another. They differ in the kind of transformation that is taking place and in the rate at which the transformation proceeds. Iron rusts quickly, silver more slowly, gold more slowly still, and platinum hardly seems to change at all. All of these metals are always combining with the oxygen in the air. For metals, the common name for this process is *rusting* or tarnishing. The chemical name is *oxidation*. All metals are continuously oxidizing, even platinum. We

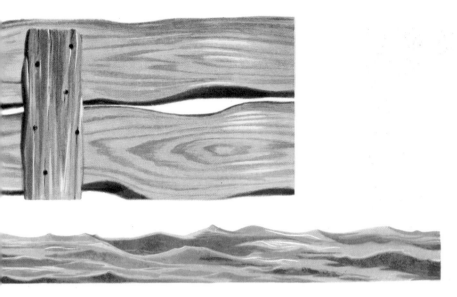

280. Some aspects of matter. *Wood, stone, water, and iron are only a few of the vast number of forms which matter assumes. Varieties of matter may be solid, liquid, or gas. They may differ in size, shape, weight, and color or may even be colorless or invisible. They resemble each other in that they all have mass and take up space.*

281. Crystal structure of aluminum oxide. *Aluminum oxide, composed of 2 atoms of aluminum (light spheres) for every 3 atoms of oxygen (dark spheres), is useful in insulators, grinding powders, porcelain, ceramic nose cones, and many other products. Its hardness, strength, and stability at high temperatures are related to its structure.*

282. Oxidation of aluminum. *The initially shiny surface of aluminum grows gray and clouded because aluminum combines with oxygen in the air to form aluminum oxide. When highly magnified, the oxide film is seen to be a tangled mass of long, hair-like crystals. Whether it is called rusting, tarnishing, dulling, or corrosion, all metals undergo oxidation to some extent upon exposure to air.*

283. Antoine-Laurent Lavoisier (1743–1794). *This great French chemist and physicist was the founder of modern chemistry. He stated the law of conservation of matter: Matter cannot be created or destroyed, only transformed. Einstein later found that matter could be converted into energy.*

cannot avoid oxidation except by removing the air. We can, however, select a metal which oxidizes slowly enough to suit our purpose.

The burning of wood or paper is a form of oxidation. Our bodies are chemical factories that use the air we breathe to oxidize the food we eat. The carbon in the food is converted into carbon dioxide, which we exhale before drawing in a fresh breathful of air.

Oxidation is not the only process by which matter is transformed. Substances break down into simpler substances or combine with others to become more complex. Frequently there is a change in form without a change in chemical nature. This happens when water evaporates to become steam or vapor or when ice melts to become water.

We saw earlier, in the book about our earth, how rocks crumble from the effects of weather, how mountains are worn down by erosion, and how water can cut through rock by scraping and dissolving the matter of which the rock is composed. No substance is immune. All substances are being transformed. It is only a question of time.

The Law of Conservation of Matter In the eighteenth century, the French chemist Lavoisier (figure 283) performed experiments that led him to certain conclusions about the behavior of matter. He formulated the *law of conservation of matter* which states that matter cannot be created or destroyed, it can only be transformed. Such an idea had already been expressed by the Greek philosopher Empedocles over 400 years before Christ, and some 2100 years before Lavoisier. Lavoisier, however, proved his statement by experiment. Whenever he observed a reaction between two or more chemicals, the weights of all the chemicals before the reaction equaled the weights of all products of the reaction. If oxygen from the air took part in the reaction, the weight of the oxygen also had to be taken into account.

Since Einstein found the relationship between matter and energy, the law of conservation of matter is no longer considered strictly true. However, for practical purposes, it is still very useful. The amount of

284. Boiling nitrogen. *Nitrogen as a gas forms approximately ⅘ of the earth's atmosphere. When cooled to 320°F below zero, it condenses into a liquid just as water becomes steam at 212°F. In an insulated flask, the cold nitrogen remains a clear, colorless liquid, but when poured, it is quickly warmed by the air to its boiling point and boils much like water heated in a kettle.*

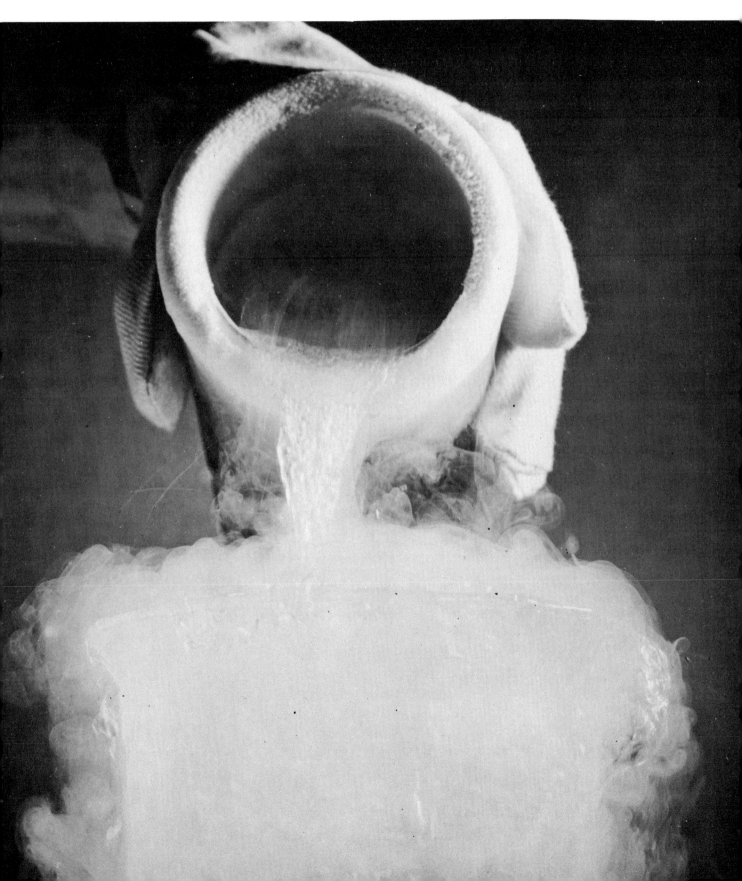

285. Molten aluminum. *Raw aluminum is poured into a mold to form a 1000-pound "sow" in an aluminum reduction plant. Aluminum is abundant in soil and rock, but it is trapped in chemical compounds. Strong electric currents are used to separate aluminum metal from tightly attached oxygen atoms in oxide ores.*

matter converted into energy, or energy converted into matter, is so small in all chemical reactions, we may ignore it in the present discussion.

To illustrate the law of conservation of matter, we do not have to talk about copper, oxygen, sulfur, iodine, or other chemicals. The law is obeyed when a boy who weighs 100 pounds stuffs himself with a pound of hamburgers. If we weigh him after he has eaten, we will find that his new weight is 101 pounds.

Chemical Elements   If we treat a substance in various ways, we find that it often splits into a number of other substances. For example, we can mix gunpowder with water, stir it, heat it, filter it, dry the remains, attack it further by various chemical and mechanical processes, and then examine the result. We will find that we now have three different substances, namely carbon, sulfur, and saltpeter (potassium nitrate). If we continue our efforts we find that we cannot reduce the carbon and sulfur further into any other substances. They remain the same. However, the saltpeter separates into three new substances, potassium, nitrogen, and oxygen. If we work further on these three substances, we find that they cannot be divided into any more parts, no matter how hard we try. We have found that gunpowder is really made of five different substances. Since these five different substances are not made of any other simpler substances, they must be the simplest parts of which substances are constructed. For this reason they are called *chemical elements*.

To date at least 103 such elements have been identified. Some 90 of these elements, alone or in combination with each other, make up almost all the substances that exist or ever will exist in nature. The other elements are unstable and survive for only a short time after being created either by nature or by man.

A cook combines the same ingredients (flour, milk, sugar, butter, and eggs) in many ways to bake different cakes. Nature combines her elemental ingredients in different proportions to manufacture the substances of the universe. Some of the elements are normally solid, like iron. Others are normally liquid, like mercury. Still others are normally gaseous, like oxygen. However, gaseous elements can be made liquid by cooling, usually under high pressures and often to very low temperatures. Liquid elements can be frozen solid. Therefore, the form or state, solid, liquid, or gas, in which an element exists, depends on conditions such as temperature and pressure. When we say that an element is "normally" solid (the silver in a spoon) or "normally" gaseous (the helium in a balloon), we are describing the element under the special conditions in which we find it in everyday life.

All pure metals are elements. These include such metals as silver, aluminum, gold, copper, iron, nickel, lead, platinum, tin, zinc, and others with less familiar names. Mixtures of metals such as brass, bronze, steel, or pewter are, of course, not elements. They are mixtures of elements.

The elements do not exist in the earth in equal amounts. Oxygen is more abundant than all the others. It is found in air, water, and in all living things. The solid part of the earth's crust consists of substances which are about 50 per cent oxygen. Nonmetallic silicon is the next most prevalent element, occurring in sand, quartz, and rocks. After silicon come nitrogen, carbon,

aluminum, iron, and the rest of the elements. Most of the elements are not found in a pure state but are locked in compounds with one or more other elements. Great blast furnaces are used to separate iron from the oxygen and other elements to which the iron is attached in the ores that are dug from the ground. Aluminum is separated from its ore by the action of large electric currents.

In addition to the earth, the elements compose the sun, the other planets, and all the stars in the universe.

The Law of Definite Proportions When nature combines elements to form substances called *compounds,* the combinations obey a strict law. A compound is different from a mere mixture of elements. In some mixtures the elements retain their own characteristics and simply rest beside each other the way sugar and salt would behave when stirred in a dry bowl. In other mixtures, like alloys of metals, the elements may mingle in a more complicated way, but still retain a certain degree of separateness and preserve many of their original characteristics. In a compound the elements join together to form a new substance which may be completely unlike any of the individual components. Ordinary salt is a compound of sodium, a silvery metal, and chlorine, a poisonous gas. Yet the compound is a white, crystalline substance that is necessary to our health. Water, a liquid, is a compound of two gases, hydrogen and oxygen.

The composition of such compounds was

319

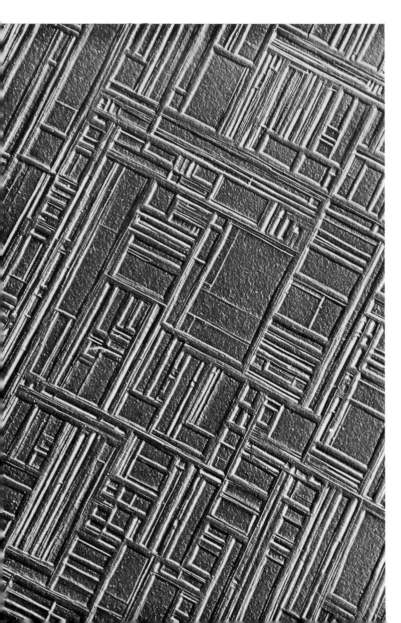

Growth of iron oxide crystals. *When iron and oxygen atoms link together in an orderly arrangement to form a new substance, an iron oxide crystal is born. The crystal grows by acquiring oxygen from the surrounding gas and by diffusion of iron from the base metal. Magnified thousands of times by an electron microscope, the crystal growth habits are seen to be strongly influenced by environment.*

ABOVE, LEFT TO RIGHT:

286. *Oxide formed on stainless steel in wet oxygen with a trace of hydrochloric acid vapor at 1110°F. Crystals are parallel plates with gracefully curved leading edges.*

287. *Oxide formed on pure iron in dry oxygen at 932°F. Crystals are a mass of billions of fine wiry whiskers. Magnification has been reduced to show the large number of crystals.*

288. *Oxide formed on pure iron in water vapor and argon atmosphere at 842°F. Crystals are long slender daggers of varying lengths rising from clusters of shorter blades at the base metal.*

289. *(Left) Thin oxide film on single crystal of iron. In early stages, the pattern is like a street map, related to the positions of the iron atoms in the crystal beneath the film. In later stages, oxide whiskers obscure the pattern.*

290. *(Right) Iron crystal surface after reduction of oxide. Removal of oxygen from the oxide whiskers frees displaced iron atoms to return to the parent iron crystal, which they cover with a pattern of terraced hills and valleys.*

320

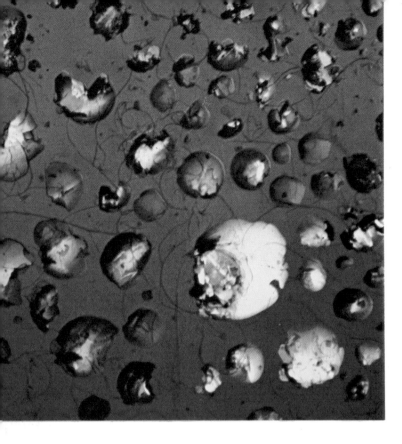 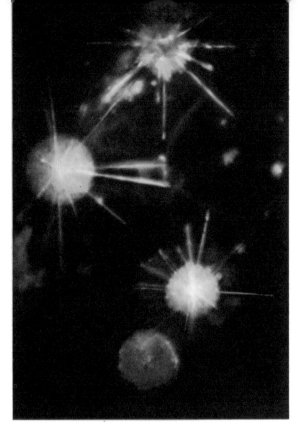

291-294. Chemical reactions. *Chemical reactions involve atoms and molecules too small to be seen. Events do occur, however, on a scale visible under the microscope, yielding information useful in understanding and controlling the reactions. Figure* *291 is a violent reaction, nearly an explosion, encountered in experiments with rocket fuel. In figure 292 particles grow arms during acid attack. Liquids combine to form plastics compounds (below and at right).*

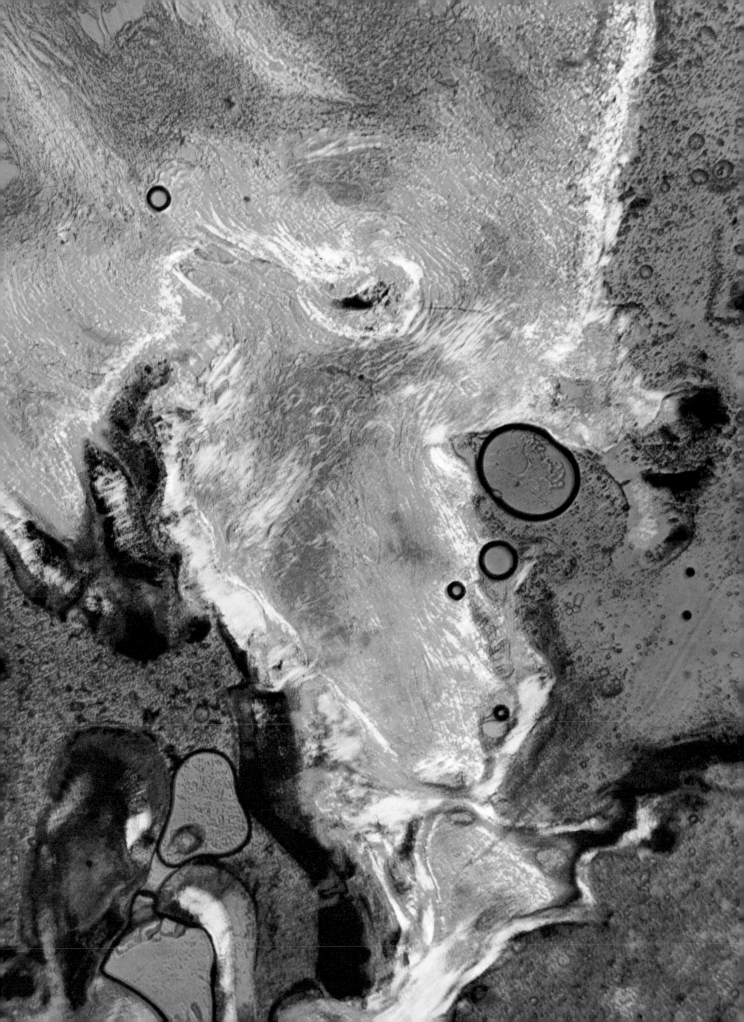

found to follow the *law of definite proportions,* formulated in 1799 by the French chemist Joseph Louis Proust. This law states that the weights of the different elements in any particular compound are always in the same proportion, no matter how the compound is prepared or where it is found. For example, if we burn 2 ounces of hydrogen, 16 ounces of oxygen are drawn from the air. The result is 18 ounces of water. In any pure water anywhere in the world, at any time, there is always 8 times as much oxygen by weight as there is hydrogen. We might try to break the law by adding an extra ounce of hydrogen to the 2 ounces we start with, seal this in a container with the same 16 ounces of oxygen, and ignite the mixture. There would be an explosion. If our container is strong enough to remain sealed, we may examine the contents. We will find that the 16 ounces of oxygen still combined with only 2 ounces of hydrogen to give the same result: 18 ounces of water. The extra ounce of hydrogen will remain free in our container. The law of definite proportions will hold.

This is true of all chemical compounds. Table salt is made of 61 per cent chlorine and 39 per cent sodium. In any 100 ounces of salt there will always be close to 61 ounces of chlorine and 39 ounces of sodium.

The Atomic Theory Other laws were discovered showing other simple rules obeyed when elements form compounds. For example, two elements frequently combine to form two or more different compounds. Of course, the proportions are different in each compound. Hydrogen and oxygen can form not only water, but also hydrogen peroxide, a chemical sometimes used as an antiseptic. We observed before that in water there is 1 part by weight of hydrogen to 8 parts of oxygen. In hydrogen peroxide there are 1 part of hydrogen and 16 parts of oxygen, just twice as much oxygen for each part of hydrogen as there is in water. In any compound a single part of hydrogen and the number of parts of oxygen that can combine with it are always in a simple whole number ratio to each other. It was found that other compounds are formed in similar ways. There always seems to be some simple relationship between the amounts of a given element that can combine with a certain amount of some other element.

Scientists puzzled over this strange tidiness of chemical behavior. Their puzzlement led to the *atomic theory of matter,* first stated clearly by John Dalton (figure 295), an English chemist. As we have seen so often, a similar idea had been suggested by the ancient Greeks as early as 500 B.C. The philosopher Leucippus had taught the first-known atomic theory to his student Democritus, who developed it further. Five hundred years later, this theory fascinated a Roman poet by the name of Lucretius, and he incorporated it into a famous poem called *De Rerum Natura* (*On the Nature of Things*).

According to this theory a piece of matter cannot be cut into smaller and smaller pieces without limit. If we could keep cutting the small bits, even after they became invisible under a microscope, we would reach a size beyond which we could not go. For example, we might split the block of wood in figure 296 into 4 parts, the 4 into 8, the 8 into 16, and so on, until we have reduced the wood to a fine powder. Imagine that we could continue grinding the powder into finer and finer particles. We would only find that we could not grind the particles as small as we would like. We would produce particles of extremely small size, the smallest size in which bits of wood can exist. It was suggested by the Greek philosophers that such small particles of matter be called *atoms* after the Greek word *atomos,* which means indivisible.

Atomic Weights of the Elements It was this theory which John Dalton revised in 1803. However, Dalton applied the name *atom* not to the particles of any substance, but specifically to the particles of an element. Dalton assumed that all chemical elements are made up of a very large number of indivisible particles called atoms. All the atoms of any one element are exactly the same as each other, but different from the atoms of any other element. Since the atoms of a particular element are all the same, they all have the same weight. This weight is different from the weights of all other kinds of atoms. Therefore, each element has a special property that belongs to it alone: the weight of one of its atoms.

The weights of atoms are, of course, extremely small. For example, it would take 17 million billion billion atoms of hydrogen

295. John Dalton (1766–1844). *The early form of the modern atomic theory of matter was first clearly expressed by this English chemist and physicist. Some of his theories concerning chemical reactions and the behavior of mixtures of gases have become fundamental laws of chemistry.*

to make one ounce. Therefore each hydrogen atom weighs

$$\frac{1}{17,000,000,000,000,000,000,000,000}$$

of an ounce.

Chemists would soon suffer from writer's cramp if they had to write such numbers when dealing with atomic weights, so they invented a more practical system. They decided to call the atomic weight of oxygen by the number 16. The atomic weights of all the other elements could be fitted into

296. Atomizing a log. *Ancient Greek philosophers were the first to suggest that a piece of wood could not be split into ever smaller bits. The imagined smallest particle that could not be divided further they called atomos, indivisible. Today we call the smallest wood particles molecules. Each wood molecule is composed of atoms of elements, mostly carbon, hydrogen, and oxygen.*

297. Chemicals absorbing water from air. *Dusty roads are often dampened by sprinkling with dry calcium chloride flakes. This is what happens: (1) Flakes are fresh from a sealed bag. (2) After 24 minutes smaller flakes are enveloped in moisture drawn from the air. (3) After 48 minutes the droplets are larger and flakes are beginning to dissolve in their own water. (4) After 3 hours all but the largest flakes are dissolved. The solution then sinks into the roadbed, wetting down the dust.*

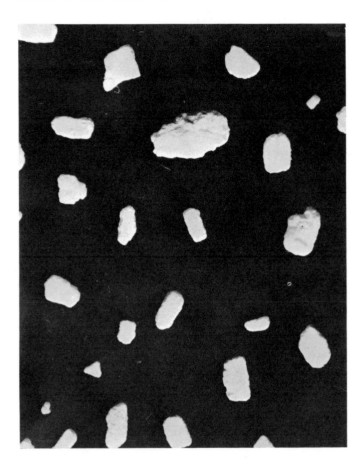
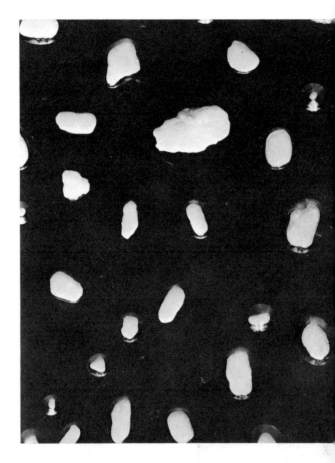
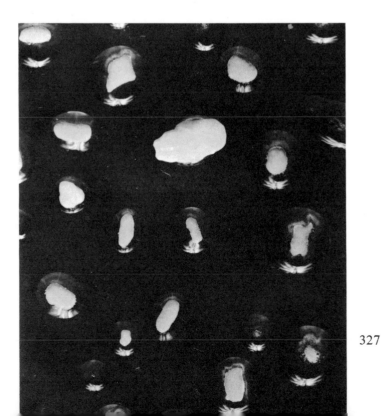

Manufacture of synthetic diamonds. *Natural diamonds are a form of carbon, related to charcoal, produced by accident with great heat and pressure deep in the earth. Man's dream of duplicating this feat came true in the General Electric Research Laboratory in 1955. Soft graphite was converted into brittle diamond in equipment specially developed to withstand enormous forces at high temperatures for extended lengths of time.*

299. Diamond-making press. *This press can exert a force of 1000 tons on the pistons which compress the graphite being changed into diamond. The tapered pistons concentrate this force over a small surface, thereby creating the high pressures needed in the process. The press is fitted with instruments for the precise control and measurement of pressures and temperatures.*

298. Model of ultra-high pressure chamber. *Pistons, tapered for greater strength, push into the small hole in the large disk, producing pressures up to 1,500,000 lbs/sq. in. Parts shown in wood are really made of carbide materials durable at high temperatures. They are strengthened by binding rings like barrel hoops which enable them to survive temperatures over 4000°F without fracturing.*

300. High-pressure sample holder assembly. (*Below*) *Diamond-making takes place in the cylinder at the center which holds the graphite and metal catalyst. Conical parts are gaskets which fit together to seal in the pressure. Gasket material would normally melt, but intense pressure raises its melting point. High temperatures are reached by passing electric current through the sample.*

ONE INCH

301. Photomicrograph of man-made diamonds. *Film of catalyst metal was removed from center diamond to show triangular face common also to many natural diamonds. First man-made diamonds were small, less than $\frac{1}{16}$ inch, but useful in industry for cutting and grinding. Without catalyst metal, pressure and temperature would have to be doubled to cause diamond formation.*

302. First large man-made diamonds. *Advanced techniques produced carat-sized diamonds. Large specimens are dark, not gem quality, and still not strong enough for industrial applications. Diamond is valuable in industry because it is the hardest known substance. The fact that synthetic diamonds can scratch natural diamonds is one proof that they are true diamonds.*

303. Diamond-tipped phonograph needle. *One application of diamonds is for tips of phonograph needles. This man-made diamond is only 0.040 inches long but can make several needles. Diamond hardness prevents wear of the needle point which can cause distortion of sound and permanent damage to the record. Diamond points can be shaped and polished only by other diamonds.*

304. Why graphite is soft and diamond is hard. *Models show arrangement of atoms in diamond and graphite crystals. Properties of diamond, such as hardness and density, are related to the close-packing and strong binding forces of its atoms. Graphite atoms are farther apart in spaced layers with weaker forces. Consequently, graphite is softer and less dense, suitable for pencil leads.*

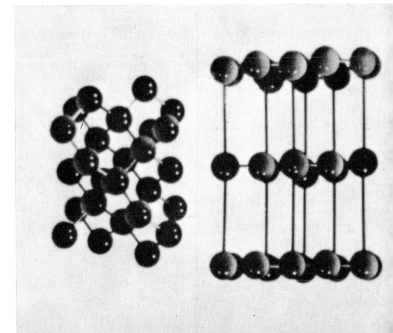

this system by determining how much lighter or heavier their atoms were than the atoms of oxygen. The number 16 was chosen because the oxygen atom is just 16 times as heavy as the lightest atom of all, that of hydrogen. Therefore, the atomic weight of hydrogen is 1 and the atomic weights of all the other elements are greater than 1. Actually, the precise atomic weight of hydrogen is not exactly 1, but it is very close: 1.008.

Oxygen was chosen as the standard against which to compare all the other atomic weights for a special reason. Oxygen is an element that combines readily with almost all the other elements to form simple compounds. One way to determine the atomic weight of an element is to find out how much of it will combine with a certain amount of another element whose atomic weight is already known. Oxygen is therefore an ideal starting point for calculating the atomic weights of the other elements. Let us examine how this process works.

According to the atomic theory, compounds are created by the joining of a definite number of atoms of one element with a definite number of atoms of one or more other elements. For example, water is a compound in which 2 atoms of hydrogen join with 1 atom of oxygen. Carbon dioxide, produced by burning carbon in air, is formed by the combination of 1 atom of carbon with 2 atoms of oxygen. We will use carbon dioxide as an example of how an unknown atomic weight is calculated.

We discover that when carbon is burned in 16 grams of oxygen, 22 grams of carbon dioxide result. (We use *grams* as a measure of weight because this is the measure most chemists use, and atomic weights are normally related to grams rather than ounces. There are 28.3 grams in an ounce.) We have now determined that there are 6 grams of carbon to every 16 grams of oxygen in carbon dioxide. From other information we also know that there is 1 carbon atom for every 2 oxygen atoms. Therefore, there are only half as many carbon atoms in 6 grams of carbon as there are oxygen atoms in 16 grams of oxygen. Twelve grams of carbon contain the same number of carbon atoms as there are oxygen atoms in 16 grams of oxygen. Since 16 is the atomic weight of oxygen, 12 is the atomic weight of carbon. If we calculated the weights of 1 carbon atom and 1 oxygen atom, they would still be in the ratio of 12 to 16.

Atoms into Molecules The cluster of exactly 1 atom of carbon and 2 atoms of oxygen is the smallest amount of carbon dioxide that can ever exist. We cannot have less than 1 carbon atom in the group because the atom cannot be divided. Moreover, there must be 2 atoms of oxygen for each atom of carbon or the compound would not be carbon dioxide. This group of 3 atoms is called a molecule of carbon dioxide.

A *molecule* of any substance is the smallest amount of that substance that can exist and still have the recognizable properties that identify it. The molecule of a compound must have two or more atoms because a compound is made of two or more

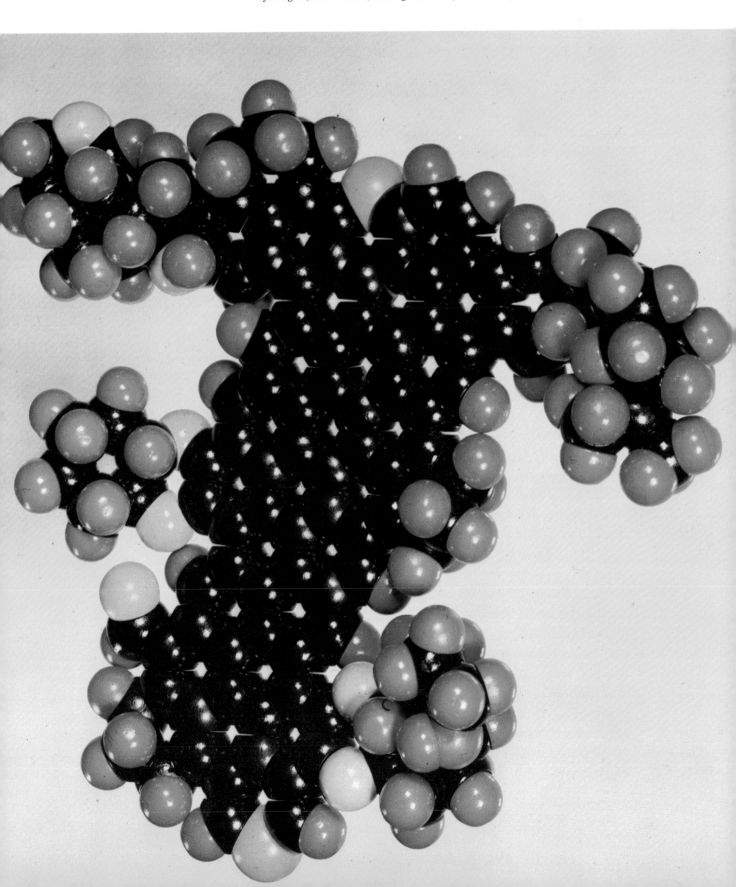

different elements. Dalton assumed that the molecule of an element was just a single atom. Since all the atoms of an element are the same, it takes only one to represent the element. We will see later how this idea had to be altered.

With the atomic theory it becomes easy to explain the law of definite proportions. Remember that, according to this law, the weights of each of the elements in any amount of a compound always make up the same percentage of the total weight. We now know that the compound is really a very large number of molecules, each exactly like all the others. In each molecule there are a definite number of atoms, so many of one kind, so many of another kind, and so on. Each kind of atom represents one of the elements present in the compound. Let us use water again as an example. Water is a compound having two different elements, hydrogen and oxygen. In each molecule there are exactly 2 atoms of hydrogen and 1 atom of oxygen. No matter how much water we have or how we make it, there are always twice as many hydrogen atoms as oxygen atoms. Each atom of oxygen weighs 16 times as much as each atom of hydrogen. Since in each molecule there are 2 hydrogen atoms to each oxygen atom, the total weight of oxygen in each molecule is 8 times the total weight of the hydrogen atoms. In any amount of water there is always 8 times as much oxygen by weight as there is hydrogen. The proportion is always the same. This is a direct illustration of the law of definite proportions.

Dalton applied the atomic theory to another law, the *law of multiple proportions.* This law deals with the situation in which different compounds are formed from the same group of elements. For example, hydrogen and oxygen also combine to give hydrogen peroxide. A molecule of hydrogen peroxide has 2 atoms of oxygen and 2 atoms of hydrogen. There is one more oxygen atom than in a molecule of water. The important fact here is that when oxygen combines with hydrogen to form more than one compound, the number of oxygen atoms in the different molecules must be 1, 2, 3, 4, or some other small whole number. If each of the molecules has the same amount of hydrogen, but different amounts of oxygen, the different amounts of oxygen must have a simple relationship to each other. They are the weights of 1, 2, 3, 4, or some other small whole number of oxygen atoms. This fact is the basis of the law of multiple proportions. The law states that when different weights of one element combine with the same weight of another element to form different compounds, the different weights of the first element are in the ratio of small whole numbers. This means that if we divide any two of the weights by each other, the fraction is a simple one like ¼, ½, ⅔, ¾, and so on.

Avogadro's Hypothesis The atomic theory of Dalton clarified the ways in which chemical elements join together to form the many different substances of the world. But scientists never reach a large new body of knowledge in just one giant step. Knowledge is

306. Birth of a solid. *Many solids are made of crystals which form when atoms or molecules come together in an orderly pattern, usually by precipitation from a solution or a vapor. In the glass beaker a supersaturated solution of a complex substance is being cooled. The solution is forced to give up some of the dissolved matter. Floating molecules or atomic clusters link together, gather more molecules, and grow into long, needle-like crystals.*

Photomicrographs of complex crystals. *Magnified as much as 120 times under polarized light, crystals display growth patterns that are both informative and beautiful. Characteristic patterns permit identification of substances and contribute to an understanding of the structure of solid bodies.*

307. Vitamin C (ascorbic acid). *The man-made chemical substitutes for natural vitamin C to prevent or cure such sicknesses as scurvy, caused by diet deficiencies.*

308. Sulfamerazine. *(Right) One of the group of sulfa drugs introduced during World War II to combat many infections, sulfamerazine was replaced by antibiotics, such as penicillin.*

309. Hydrocortisone. *(Below) This laboratory duplication of a body hormone, together with cortisone, a similar drug, is used in the treatment of more diseases than any other single substance.*

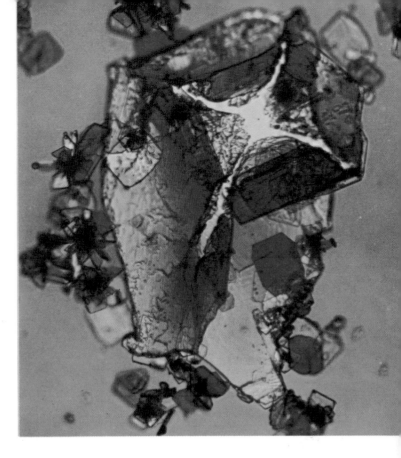

always the work of many men, each building on the progress of the one before. The man who carried Dalton's work forward was Amedeo Avogadro (figure 310).

Avogadro's great achievement was actually a correction of one of Dalton's ideas. We mentioned before that Dalton assumed that all elements were composed of small particles and that these particles were single atoms. This idea was accepted by most chemists, along with the rest of the atomic theory. However, many contradictions and difficulties arose. These led the Italian chemist and physicist, Avogadro, to question Dalton's assumption. In 1811 Avogadro proposed a different principle, now called *Avogadro's hypothesis*. He suggested that the elements might not all be collections of single atoms. Some of them might actually be composed of units made up of groups of atoms bound together. For instance, metallic elements like mercury, sodium, zinc, and potassium might be made up of single atoms, but gaseous elements like hydrogen, oxygen, nitrogen, and chlorine are clouds of particles which are really molecules with two atoms in each molecule. Avogadro went so far as to suggest that some elements were constructed of molecules with as many as 4 or even 8 atoms. This picture of the structure of matter was more complex than Dalton's. It did not contradict the basic atomic theory, but it did change some of Dalton's interpretations of this theory.

For some reason Avogadro's hypothesis was not immediately accepted. As a result, the contradictions multiplied between the

310. Amedeo Avogadro (1776–1856). *Avogadro's famous hypothesis held that equal volumes of all gases at the same temperature and pressure contained the same number of molecules, and that each molecule was composed of one or more of Dalton's atoms. The number of molecules in a standard amount of any gas is called Avogadro's number.*

Dalton theory, which was accepted, and the experimental evidence that chemists accumulated in their laboratories. The entire atomic theory was in danger of being discarded. J. B. Dumas, the leader of the French school of chemistry, said he would remove the word "atom" from the dictionary if he could.

It was almost 50 years later that Avogadro's hypothesis was revived by a young Italian chemist named Stanislao Cannizzaro. In 1860, at a scientific meeting in Karlsruhe, Germany, before chemists from many nations, Cannizzaro presented his views, clearly distinguishing between atoms and molecules. The rebirth of the ideas of Avogadro saved the atomic theory and scattered the confusion that had been blocking progress. It was recognized that atoms were still the smallest building blocks from which matter was constructed. Beyond this, it was also recognized that when elements exist freely in nature, their atoms may join together in little groups of two or more atoms each.

Too Many Zeros We have already given an indication of how small atoms and molecules are. Now let us ask how many molecules of a gas are flying about in the space inside an empty quart milk bottle. The answer is 30 thousand billion billion, or

$$30,000,000,000,000,000,000,000$$

There are too many zeros for convenience, yet chemists and physicists must use such numbers frequently. The numbers for the size or weight of tiny particles, the distances to stars, the years of geological eras, and other quantities in science often require many zeros. Therefore, a simple shorthand system has been developed whereby such numbers may be written quickly, easily, and accurately.

The system is based on the idea of *powers* of 10. Ten to the first power is the number 10 itself. Ten to the second power is 10 times itself once, that is, 10×10. Therefore, 10 to the second power is 100. Ten to the third power is $10 \times 10 \times 10$ which is 1000. This is written as follows

$$10^1 = 10$$
$$10^2 = 10 \times 10 = 100$$
$$10^3 = 10 \times 10 \times 10 = 1000$$
$$10^4 = 10 \times 10 \times 10 \times 10 = 10,000$$

and so on for as long as you like.

The power to which 10 is raised is the figure written just above and to the right of the 10. It signifies the number of tens that are to be multiplied together. Notice that this power is also the same as the number of zeros in the figure at the far right. For example, 10^4 is a number written as a 1 followed by four zeros, which is 10,000. To write any large number that is made up of a few digits followed by many zeros, we count the number of zeros first. Then we write the digits but replace all the zeros by 10 raised to the proper power. This proper power is the number of zeros.

For example, take the number of molecules in the empty milk bottle. This is a 3 followed by twenty-two zeros. We can write this number simply as

$$3 \times 10^{22}$$

Suppose we wish to shorten the number representing the speed of light, 186,000 miles per second. We can write this as

$$186 \times 10^3 \text{ miles per second}$$

Now suppose the number is very small, very much less than 1. We can write such a number as a decimal in the form of a decimal point followed by many zeros and then ending with the final digits, for example, 0.0000000095. The zero to the left of the decimal point does not add anything to the number. It is written as a matter of form. The shorthand way of writing powers of 10 for small numbers is as follows

$$10^0 = 1$$
$$10^{-1} = 1/10^1 = 1/10 = 0.1$$

$$10^{-2}=1/10^2=1/100=0.01$$
$$10^{-3}=1/10^3=1/1000=0.001$$
$$10^{-4}=1/10^4=1/10,000=0.0001$$

and so on. Ten raised to a minus power is the number 1 divided by 10 raised to the plus power. Ten raised to the zero power is taken to be the number 1 itself. Notice that the number 0.0001 is the same as 1×10^{-4}. Imagine that we have moved the decimal point four places to the right to arrive at the number 1. To account for this movement of four places we multiply the 1 by 10^{-4}. The method is to move the decimal point as many places to the right as we like and then write the number that is left multiplied by 10 raised to a minus power. The power is the number of places the decimal point was moved.

Let us use the number 0.0000000095 as another example. If we move the decimal point eight places to the right, we pass by the eight zeros to leave 0.95. We can write the number as 0.95×10^{-8}. If we had moved the decimal point nine places, we would have been left with 9.5. The number would then be written as 9.5×10^{-9}. We could also write the number as 95×10^{-10}, because this would represent moving the decimal point ten places to the right.

The Mass of a Molecule We need a system of writing very small numbers to describe the masses or weights of atoms and molecules. For example, the mass of a water molecule is almost exactly 3×10^{-23} grams.

We can calculate the masses of molecules and learn about their behavior largely as a consequence of the usefulness of Avogadro's hypothesis together with Dalton's atomic theory. For example, we know that in a given space occupied by any gas, there are always the same number of molecules, no matter which gas it is. In particular, in a volume of 22.4 liters (a *liter* is a little less than a quart) at normal temperature and pressure, there are 6.02×10^{23} molecules of gas. In honor of Avogadro, this is called *Avogadro's number*.

The Restless Molecules Our bodies and all the things around us are merely great collections of molecules. The molecules, in turn, are groups of one or more atoms. The molecules are the tiny bricks of which we are built. What are these molecules doing?

Molecules are forever in motion. They never stand still. How far they can travel in their motion depends on the nature of the body that contains them. In a solid material the molecules are bound tightly together by forces of attraction. They are locked in position and can only vibrate back and forth a little, always being pulled back toward that position when they tend to stray off. Since the molecules do not wander, the solid maintains its shape.

In a liquid, the molecules are farther apart from each other. They still attract one another a little so they are not completely free to roam as they wish. However, they have greater freedom than in a solid. As a result, they take longer excursions and may drift about without being tied to one spot. Because its molecules do wander, a

311. Super-purification of metals. *For modern devices such as the transistor, zone refining produces metals of incredible purity, as few as one foreign atom per billion atoms of metal. Only a segment of the metal bar is melted by the induc-* *tion coil. Impurity atoms are set adrift and flow toward one end of the segment. As the bar is slowly pulled through the heating zone, the impurities are gradually swept out of the bar to concentrate at one end.*

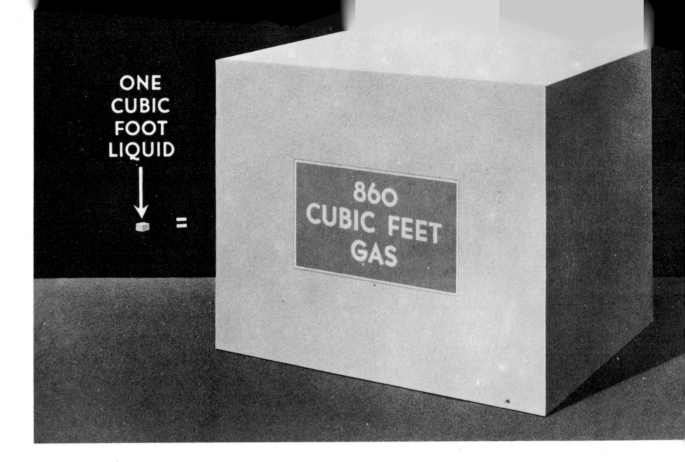

ONE
CUBIC
FOOT
LIQUID

860
CUBIC FEET
GAS

312. Oxygen volume as a liquid and a gas. *When oxygen gas is cooled, its molecules move more slowly and the pressure falls. If the container is shrunk to keep a constant pressure, the gas fills less space and the molecules are closer together. At 297°F below zero the molecules come so close, the gas condenses to a liquid. 860 cubic feet of gas form one cubic foot of liquid, but both weigh the same.*

liquid is able to flow to fill the lower portions of its container.

The molecules of a gas are very far from one another, compared to the molecules in a liquid or a solid. They hold almost no attraction for one another. Therefore, a molecule proceeding in a particular direction will not be pulled back by the attractive force of its neighbors. It will continue in that direction until it collides with other molecules or the walls of the container. In this event, the molecule will not stop. It will rebound and dash off in another direction until the next collision. Because of

the freedom of motion of its molecules, a gas can spread to the far corners of any enclosure the way air fills a room from floor to ceiling and wall to wall.

As a good example of the behavior of molecules in all three forms of matter, let us consider ice. Ice is a solid. The molecules are cold. Temperature is really a measure of the motion of molecules. In cold bodies the molecules are relatively slow (although still fast compared with the speeds we are used to). In warmer bodies, the molecules move faster. The heat energy that is put into a body to warm it up is converted into the energy of motion of the molecules of the body. The cold molecules of ice do not move fast enough to pull away from the position to which they are confined by the surrounding molecules. The molecules quiver a little but remain in place. Therefore, the ice does not change shape. Now heat the ice. The molecules

340

speed up. They vibrate faster and to farther distances from their average positions. When enough heat is supplied, the molecules can actually pull away from these positions and the solid body can no longer hold together. It becomes a liquid, water, and flows. Gravity pulls the liquid to the bottom of the container. The liquid cannot rise out of the container, but it can spread sideways.

Now we heat the water. The molecules pick up still more speed and dash about with more vigor, up, down, right, left. Some can actually leap above the surface of the water if they happen to be traveling upward when they are near the surface and if there are few molecules above them to interfere with their upward motion. This upward escape from the liquid to the space above the surface is called *evaporation*.

313. Critical temperatures of liquids. *At normal atmospheric pressure, oxygen condenses to a liquid at −297°F, nitrogen at −320°F, and argon at −303°F. They must be stored at these low temperatures or they will boil away into gases once more. Under high pressure, they will remain liquid at higher temperatures.*

Evaporation is always taking place at the surface of a liquid (even at the surface of solids), but is increased when the addition of heat raises the temperature of the liquid and the average speed of its molecules. This explains why a wet sidewalk dries faster in the summer than on an equally dry but colder day in winter. When we heat the water to 212° F, the molecules race about so fast they break free of restraining forces, batter their neighbors apart, and become gas molecules. We say that the water boils. The liquid changes into steam, a gas. This gas is invisible. The smoky vapor rising from a teapot, which we loosely call steam, is the gas molecules condensed into visible droplets by the surrounding cooler air.

We can see now why a substance has the form of a solid, liquid, or gas. It is a question of a balance between the motion of the molecules and the forces between molecules that tend to hold them in fixed positions. Since the forces are not the same for all kinds of molecules, different substances have different melting and boiling temperatures.

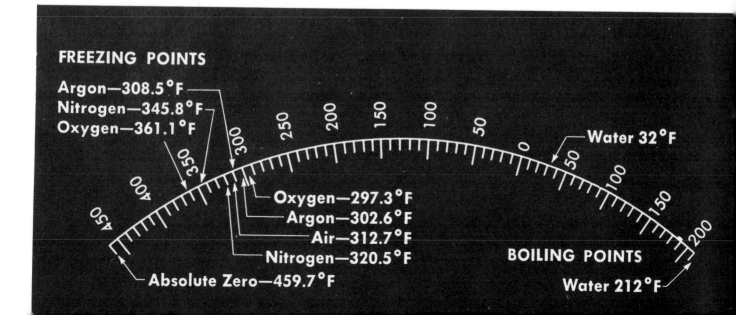

FREEZING POINTS
Argon—308.5°F
Nitrogen—345.8°F
Oxygen—361.1°F

Oxygen—297.3°F
Argon—302.6°F
Air—312.7°F
Nitrogen—320.5°F
Absolute Zero—459.7°F

Water 32°F

BOILING POINTS
Water 212°F

314. Brownian motion. *Brightly lit dust particles in a clear liquid are visible under the microscope as pinpoints of light performing a zigzagging dance. The particles dance because they are struck by molecules of the liquid which are themselves too small to be seen. The motion was named after its discoverer, Robert Brown, a Scottish botanist who also discovered the nucleus in a living cell.*

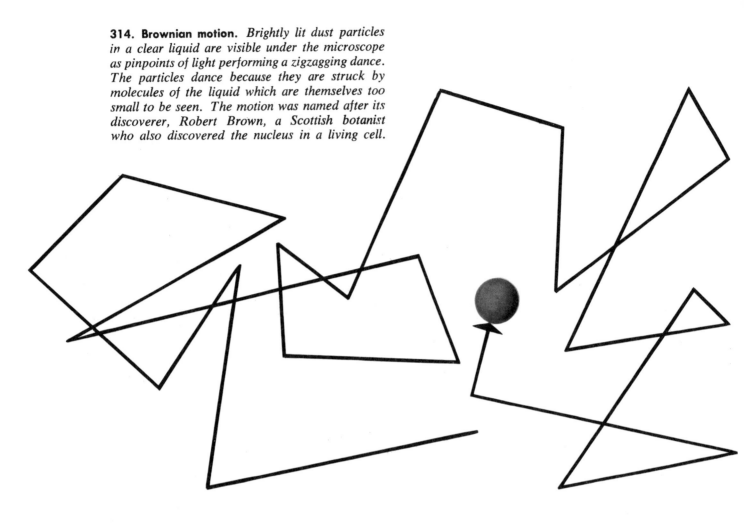

Traffic Conditions In a Gas In a gas, the molecules are free, fast, and disorderly. They rush here and there, never in a straight line for very long, always in a zigzag because of innumerable collisions with other molecules. A gas molecule lives a life of continuous traffic accidents. Although an oxygen molecule under normal air conditions travels at a speed of almost 900 miles per hour, it does not move very far. Its motion is a series of short, jerky sprints between collisions. The collisions deflect the molecule back or off to one side so that it cannot make headway. The molecule is like a man, late for an appointment, trying frantically to beat his way through a rush-hour crowd.

If a gas is confined in some kind of enclosure, the molecules continually collide with the walls of the container. The walls are bombarded by great numbers of molecules, and there are so many collisions in a single second that the sum of all the little impacts of individual molecules is felt as a continuous pressure. *Pressure* is the cumulative pounding of little molecules. When we blow up a balloon, the balloon expands because the air molecules are hammering at the walls of their rubber prison. If we heat the air in the balloon by holding it over a hot radiator, we speed up the molecules. Since they move faster, they hit the rubber harder and more often. The pressure increases and the rubber stretches even farther.

As we suggested before, a similar motion occurs in a liquid, but with some differences. In a liquid, the molecules are closer together, the crowd is thicker. There is little room for a wandering molecule to dash through an opening in the surrounding crowd of molecules. Instead, the motion is one of slipping and gliding of one molecule past another. It was in a liquid, however, that evidence of the agitation of molecules was first seen directly by the human eye. The experiment was performed by a Scottish botanist named Robert Brown in 1829.

Brown focused his microscope on fine dust particles suspended in a clear liquid. Because the liquid was brightly lit by a lamp, the particles appeared as little pinpoints of light. The pinpoints did not drift about gently the way dust in the air drifts on a mild breeze. They performed a jerky, zigzag motion, up, down, here, there, backwards, forwards, like an insane dance. In honor of its discoverer, this phenomenon is known as *Brownian motion* (figure 314).

What we see under the microscope in Brownian motion is not the motion of molecules but a motion caused by them. The dust particles are large enough to be seen with the microscope. But they are also small enough to be knocked about by the bombardment of molecules which themselves are too small to be seen. Brownian motion is therefore an indirect image of molecular motion.

Facts About Air Molecules Air is made up mostly of oxygen and nitrogen molecules, about 21 per cent oxygen and 78 per cent nitrogen. However, there are some molecules of almost every other gas mixed with the air along with many varieties of dust. Therefore, we really cannot speak about a single kind of air molecule and say that it has such a size or so much weight. We would have to describe separately each kind of molecule in the mixture. We can say, however, that most simple air molecules weigh about 10^{-24} ounces. This means that the number of these molecules in one ounce of air is a 1 followed by twenty-four zeros.

The molecules in the air we breathe travel with the speed of bullets, but move only about one-millionth of an inch between collisions with other molecules. Each molecule suffers about 5 billion collisions every second. The number of collisions is great because there are so many molecules in even a small amount of space. Under normal conditions, in a *cubic inch* of air (a little square-cornered block of space 1 inch wide $\times$ 1 inch long $\times$ 1 inch deep) there are almost 500 billion billion (5×10^{20}) molecules. Even if we pump the air out of a glass tube in the best vacuum system on earth, there still remain almost 200 billion molecules in each cubic inch. In such a vacuum, the molecules have much more room to move about and the frequency of collisions is reduced. This increases the length of the straight-line path traveled by

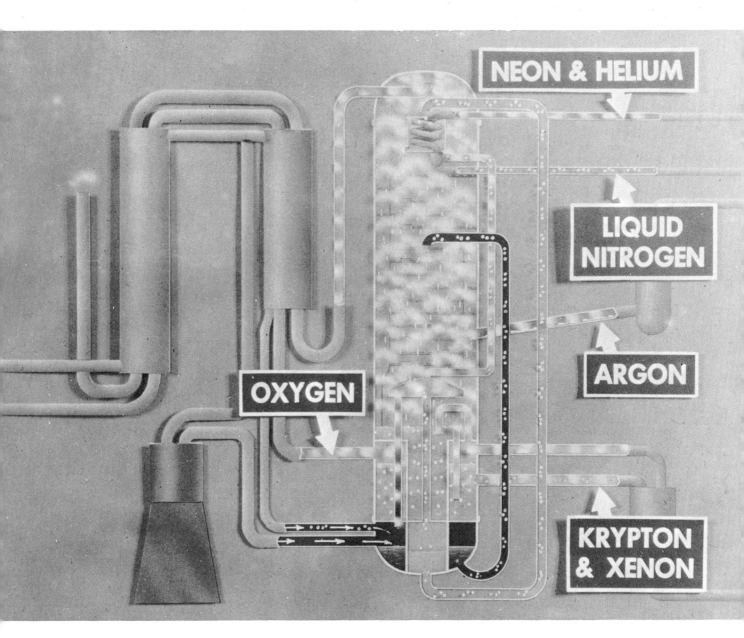

315. Separation of gases from air. *Air is almost entirely nitrogen and oxygen but also contains traces of rare gases like argon, helium, neon, krypton, and xenon. They are mixed but not chemically joined: To separate the gases, air is cooled until it becomes liquid (312.7°F below zero) and then is allowed to warm slowly. Since each liquefied gas has a different boiling point, it alone evaporates from the mixture when its boiling point is reached.*

a molecule before it bumps into another molecule.

You may wonder how it is possible to describe the motion of an extremely small particle which we cannot even see. Actually, we are only guessing at the behavior of each individual molecule. What we can

344

measure with precision is the over-all behavior of great numbers of molecules. For example, a wind is a motion of air in a certain direction at a certain speed. Yet the molecules in that air are really traveling in all directions at many different speeds. Some are going backwards, some to the side, and some in the direction of the wind. Yet the large mass of air has a general drift in only one direction. You might think of a large hive full of bees being carried along by a beekeeper. The swarm of bees moves with the man. Yet if we looked at individual bees, we would find them buzzing about in all directions.

A similar situation exists every time statistics are gathered on large groups of the population. The statistics show general trends which we call averages. We may talk of average height, average weight, average age, average death rate, average income, averge number of cars per family, and so on. A particular person may have very different characteristics from the average. For example, suppose that the average number of cars per family were one and a half. This does not mean that there is any family that has one and a half cars. It does mean that if you divide the number of cars by the number of families, you arrive at one and a half cars per family. The population as a whole behaves with much greater regularity, orderliness, and consistency than does any one person in it. The thieves are balanced by the honest people, the rich by the poor, the fat by the lean, the sick by the healthy.

With molecules, too, the jerky motion of individual molecules is smoothed out when we consider the motion of large populations of molecules. All the molecules do not move in the same direction at the same speed. They move in all directions and have a wide range of different speeds. When we say that molecules travel a millionth of an inch between collisions, we mean that many travel less than this and many travel more than this distance. It is only when we apply statistics to the behavior of large numbers of molecules that we can discover simple laws which molecules obey. We determine the average speed of the molecules by measuring the temperature of a gas. We measure the weights of the molecules by knowing the speed and measuring the pressure the molecules exert on the walls of their container. Knowing the weights of the molecules, we can weigh a certain volume of gas and calculate how many molecules there must be to add up to this total weight. If we know how many molecules there are in a certain volume of gas and how fast they move on the average, we can then calculate how many times they bump into each other in one second, again on the average.

Now that we are better acquainted with molecules and have some picture of how they behave, let us look inside them. We already know that molecules are made up of atoms so we will concentrate our attention on the inner structure of the atoms. This is the subject of the next section.

Atoms and Atomic Radiation

The Atom Proves to Be Misnamed New parents sometimes select a grand name for their baby, hoping he will grow up to suit his name. Sometimes they guess incorrectly. We all know people whose names unfortunately contradict their personalities. The men who named the atom also guessed incorrectly.

The word atom means indivisible, not capable of being separated into smaller parts. As late as the second half of the last century the atom held true to its name. Then, to their surprise, scientists discovered that pieces of metal could emit small, electrically charged particles. These particles were much smaller and lighter in weight than atoms and seemed to be thrown off by the atoms themselves. The atoms could no longer be considered indivisible. Although the meaning behind the name atom no longer applied to their true nature, it was too late to change. Atoms are called atoms to this day.

Crookes Tube This is what happened. Some early experiments of Michael Faraday had already cast doubt on the indivisibility of the atom, but these were generally ignored. Then, in 1879, Sir William Crookes, an English physicist, noticed something peculiar in some experiments he was performing with sealed glass tubes that now bear his name. A Crookes tube has a metal electrode sealed inside each end and contains a gas at very low pressure (figure 316). A voltage is applied between the electrodes, one end being positive, the other negative. The positive

316. Crookes tube. *In a similar tube, Sir William Crookes discovered cathode rays during his study of electrical discharges in gases at low pressure. The rays are electrons streaming from the cathode toward the anode, producing light by collisions with gas molecules. Damaged gas molecules, now positively charged, stream back toward the cathode, pass through the holes, and create the streaks called canal rays on the far side of the cathode.*

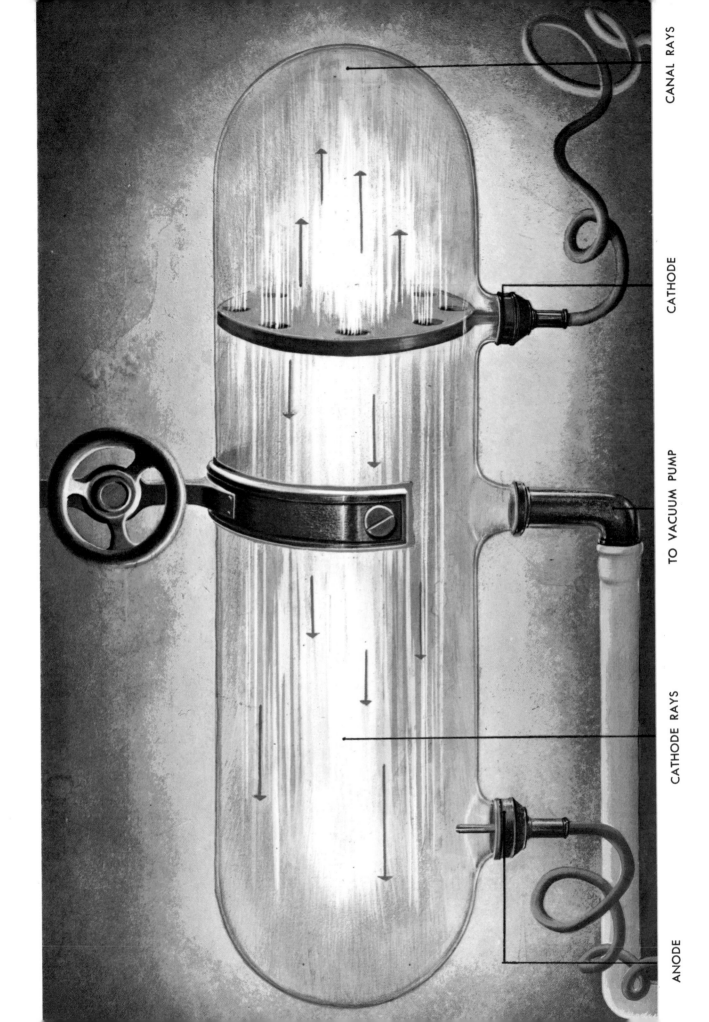

CANAL RAYS

CATHODE

TO VACUUM PUMP

CATHODE RAYS

ANODE

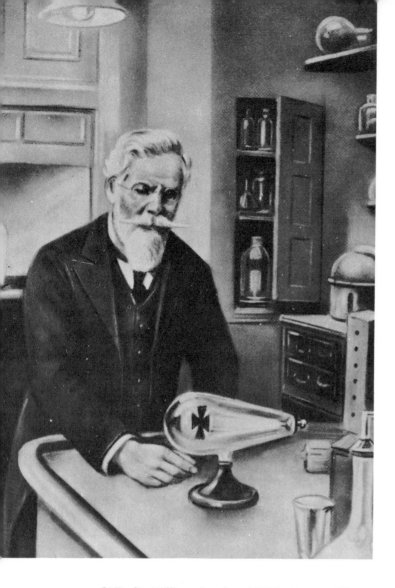

317. Sir William Crookes (1832–1919). *The famous English physicist and chemist played a large part in the rapid scientific advances that marked the turn of the century. He discovered the element thallium, studied the series of substances called the rare earths, invented the radiometer, and developed the Crookes tube for the investigation of electric discharges in gases at very low pressures.*

electrode is called the *anode*. The negative electrode is the *cathode*. As the voltage is increased, the thin gas at first acts like an insulator and almost no electric current flows between the electrodes. When the voltage is raised high enough, an electrical discharge occurs. A current passes between the electrodes and the gas glows.

You are familiar with such tubes under another name, neon lights, so called when the gas in the tube is neon. The glowing gas in a Crookes tube may have various colors—brilliant red, bright green, soft blue, orange, and so on—depending on the gas used. Neon gas provides the characteristic red color that is most common in advertising signs. The modern neon tube is much longer than a Crookes tube, is bent into many shapes, and contains some extra parts. However, the two are essentially the same.

What Crookes noticed was that a further lowering of the pressure in the tube caused the glowing light to change. . The glow would break up into stripes of light. Then as the pressure was reduced even more, the stripes would fade, the glow near the cathode would move away and a greenish fluorescence would appear in the glass near the cathode, on the side toward the anode. At still lower pressures, the greenish light in the glass would spread throughout the tube. The greenish light disappeared when the current was turned off. When a small piece of metal, shaped like a cross, was sealed in the tube between the cathode and the green region, the shadow of the cross appeared on the glass. Crookes concluded that the cathode emitted rays of some kind that traveled in straight lines and caused the glass to fluoresce where they struck the wall of the tube. Since they came from the cathode, they were called *cathode rays*.

Were Crookes' strange rays electromagnetic like light, some new kind of wave, or were they a shower of particles, bits of matter spewed out of the cathode? If they were particles, what kind were they? The scientists took to their laboratories and found the answers. Cathode rays were a stream of particles, each 1800 times lighter in weight than the hydrogen atom, the lightest of all atoms. The particles carried a negative electric charge. Their electric charge was the smallest amount of charge known to exist.

The particles were found to be identical to one another and always the same, no matter what metal was used in the cathode and no matter what gas filled the tube. They were a part of every kind of atom.

These particles with the smallest mass and smallest electric charge (other than zero) were given the name *electrons*. We now know that electric currents are a flow of electrons. The electrons are so small they can move through solid matter between the atoms as if the atoms were as far apart as the stars in the sky. When metals are heated to high temperatures, they emit greater and greater quantities of electrons as they become hotter and hotter. Radioactive materials shoot out fast electrons. Electrons are knocked out of metal surfaces by ultraviolet light. Great swarms of electrons stream out of the sun and some of them enter the earth's atmosphere. Electrons are everywhere and no matter where they come from, they are always the same.

We cannot see electrons, but we can easily see the result of their work. The wire in an electric light bulb becomes hot because electrons are being forced through the wire. The screen on your television set lights up because the coating on the inside of the picture tube is being struck by flying electrons. You receive a little shock if you touch metal after walking across a thick rug, because the friction of your shoes separates electrons from the atoms in the rug and you gather an electric charge as you walk. A similar thing happens when you slide over the seat covers of an automobile and reach for the door handle.

Positive Rays Now that the electron was discovered and was understood to be a component of all atoms, what made up the rest of the atom? Physicists did not think for a moment that the atom was composed of electrons alone. The atom as a whole was electrically neutral and carried no electric charge. If it contained negative electrons, there must be other parts of the atom that were positively charged to cancel the charge of the electrons.

This deduction was soon shown to be true. The discovery was again made in a Crookes tube which had been modified. The cathode was made of a flat metal disk with a number of holes in it, as in figure 316. In 1886 a German scientist, Eugen Goldstein, observed streaks of light in the gas behind the cathode. The streaks sometimes reached the glass at the back end of the tube, the end away from the anode. This caused the glass at this end to fluoresce.

These streaks were different from cathode rays. Cathode rays, or electrons, originated in the cathode and streamed toward the anode, striking the walls of the tube between cathode and anode. These new rays appeared to originate in the gas between cathode and anode and to race back toward the cathode. Where there were holes, the rays passed through to the region behind the cathode. The streaks of light they produced seemed to extend from the holes in the cathode.

There were other differences. Cathode rays produced green light in the glass. The new rays produced light in the gas behind the cathode that was characteristic of the gas in the tube. The color changed with a change of gas. Both rays were affected by a magnet, but the cathode rays bent one way and the new rays bent the other way. An even more striking difference existed. The electrons in cathode rays were always the same, having the same weight and the same electric charge in every experiment. The new rays had a weight that was very close to the weight of an atom of the gas in the tube, or sometimes the weight of a molecule of the gas.

The new rays were first called *canal rays,* the holes in the cathode representing the canals through which the rays flowed. Soon it was recognized that the rays were particles, actually atoms of gas, with a positive electric charge. They received another name, *positive rays.*

After further experiments the origin of the positive rays became clear. The electrical discharge between cathode and anode was so violent, it knocked electrons out of the atoms of the gas. Since the atoms were formerly neutral electrically, having no net charge, they became positive when they lost a negative electron. The electrons that were knocked off the gas atoms mixed with the cathode ray electrons to which they were similar in all respects. The now positively charged atoms, lacking one or sometimes more electrons, streamed in the opposite direction. Negative electrons were attracted to the positive anode. Positive particles were attracted to the negative cathode. This was direct evidence that there were positive atomic particles.

Summing Up So Far Let us now sum up what was known about the atom so far. Atoms contained electrons. Electrons were particles with a negative electrical charge and were much smaller than an atom. The atoms themselves were electrically neutral. The sum of all the charges in an atom was zero. Therefore, the atom also contained positively charged particles such that the amount of positive charge was exactly equal and opposite to the amount of negative charge. Atoms could acquire a positive charge by losing one or more electrons. The amount of the positive charge was equal to the amount of charge on the missing electrons. It also seemed logical that most of the weight of the atom was made up of the positively charged parts. The electrons were much too light to play such a part.

The Plum-Pudding Atom But how are the negative and positive charges arranged inside the atom? A possibility was pro-

350

posed by Sir J. J. Thomson, the famous English physicist who had done most to confirm the existence of the electron. Thomson suggested that the heavy part of the atom might be spread uniformly throughout a small, round ball of positive electricity. He supposed that the electrons might be embedded here and there in the ball. Since the electrons were considered to be stuck in the ball like raisins in a pudding, Thomson's suggestion came to be known as the *plum-pudding atom*.

It was Ernest Rutherford (figure 318), a brilliant scientist and one of the founders of modern atomic physics, who proved that Thomson's plum-pudding atom was not correct. Rutherford's proof was based on what one might expect to happen if a positive particle were shot at a group of atoms. When a positive particle approaches an atom, it is attracted by the negative electrons and repelled by the positive portions of the atom. If the positive and negative parts of the atom are spread thin over the entire atom, the oncoming positive particle can penetrate the atom and pass through. Its path will be curved slightly because the forces attracting and

318. Ernest Rutherford (1871–1937). *Lord Rutherford originated the representation of an atom as a dense, positively charged nucleus about which electrons revolve like planets about the sun. For his research in radioactivity he was awarded the Nobel Prize in 1908.*

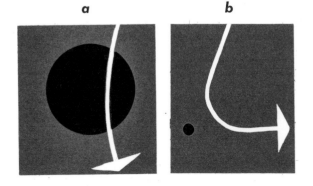

a   b

319. Path of an alpha particle through an atom. *A heavy, positively charged alpha particle would be deflected only slightly by the widely dispersed electricity in the Thomson model of the atom (a). In the Rutherford model (b), the positive charge concentrated at the atomic center would sharply repel the incoming particle. The Rutherford model agrees with experiments. The Thomson model does not.*

351

repelling it in the atom are not in perfect balance. This is shown in figure 319a.

Rutherford found that this did not happen. Instead, the positive particle sometimes underwent very sharp changes in direction (figure 319b), sometimes even rebounding straight back like a marble off a bowling ball. The positive particle that Rutherford used for a bullet was an alpha ray that is emitted naturally by some radioactive substances. The atoms which he used for a target were the atoms in an extremely thin sheet of metal.

Rutherford showed mathematically that his results agreed with the assumption that the entire positive charge in the atom was packed tightly into a little dense core at the center of the atom. His positively charged bullets were bouncing off this highly concentrated core. The electrons surrounded the core, or nucleus, in some unknown fashion. Since the electrons were so light in weight, the positive particle which was shot at the atom simply plowed through them like a cannon ball through a swarm of gnats.

The Atomic Planetary System Rutherford replaced the plum-pudding atom with one having an internal planetary system. The sun was the dense nucleus. The planets were the electrons which swirled about the nucleus. In the heavenly planetary system it is the gravitational attraction between the sun and the planets that keeps the planets in orbit. In the newly discovered atomic planetary system, it was the electrical force of attraction between the positive nucleus and the negative electrons that kept the electrons in orbit.

The parallel between the two planetary systems seemed perfect, despite the fact that one was gravitational and the other electrical. A little later we will find out that this comparison was not valid.

Over 100 Different Atomic Suns In the light of Rutherford's discovery, what do we mean when we say that there are at least 103 different elements and that the atoms of one element are different from the atoms of all other elements? We already know that atoms of different elements have different weights. Since almost all of the weight of an atom lies in its nucleus, the nuclei of different atoms must have different weights. It was found that the nuclei also have different amounts of positive electrical charge.

Since the charge carried by a nucleus is a very important number, let us describe it in a clear and simple way. We will call the smallest amount of positive charge that exists a charge of $+1$. The charge carried by an electron is exactly equal to this smallest charge but opposite in sign, that is -1. All electrical charges are simply multiples of the unit charge. When we say that the charge on the nucleus of an oxygen atom is $+8$, we mean that the nucleus carries a charge equal to 8 unit charges.

Since a complete atom is electrically neutral with the sum of all its charges equal to zero, an atom of oxygen with a charge of $+8$ on its nucleus must contain 8 electrons with a total charge of -8.

This is a fundamental fact about all atoms. The charge on the nucleus equals the number of electrons in the atom.

The over 100 different elements correspond to over 100 different kinds of atoms. The atoms of one element differ from the atoms of another element in the positive charge on their nuclei and consequently in the number of electrons in orbit about the nuclei.

The Proton Hydrogen, the lightest of all atoms, has a special importance. Its nucleus has a charge of $+1$. The atom therefore contains only 1 electron. The nucleus of the hydrogen atom carries the smallest amount of positive charge that exists in nature. It is the positive equivalent of the negative electron. Because of this, it is given the special name of *proton*.

We learned before that the atomic weight of hydrogen is 1. Since the electron has almost no weight at all, it is the proton which has this weight. The proton is therefore one of the basic particles of physics. It has a charge of $+1$ and a weight of 1 on the atomic weight scale.

The electron and the proton are two simple bricks with which nature builds the atoms of all the elements. We will learn of a third brick a little later.

Elements and Electrons After hydrogen, which has a nuclear charge of $+1$ and 1 electron, the next simplest atom is that of helium. A helium atom has a charge of $+2$ on its nucleus and therefore has 2 electrons revolving about the nucleus. Al-though the helium nucleus contains 2 protons, only twice the number in a hydrogen nucleus, the helium atom is 4 times as heavy as the hydrogen atom. This extra weight will be explained in a section to come.

After helium there is lithium with a nuclear charge of $+3$ and 3 electrons, then beryllium with a charge of $+4$ and 4 electrons, and so on. As we proceed from element to element, the charge on the nucleus goes up one unit at a time, never missing a step. The number of electrons also rises one at a time. We finally reach the atom of uranium, the most complex of all the atoms known to the scientists of the last century. The uranium nucleus contains 92 protons with a total charge of $+92$ and 92 electrons whirling about the center.

It takes a difference of only one electron, more or less, to make one element very different from another. The charge on the nucleus, which is equal to the number of electrons in the atom, is called the *atomic number*. The element with an atomic number of 79 has an atom with 79 electrons. This is gold, a precious metal which is solid and yellow. The atom with 80 electrons belongs to mercury, also a metal, but much less precious, which has the form of a silvery liquid.

Ionized Atoms We have emphasized that an atom is electrically neutral. The sum of all the charges in an atom is zero because the positive and negative charges are equal and opposite and cancel each other.

However, in our discussion of the Crookes tube, we saw how an atom could be damaged. The electrons on the outskirts of the atom, relatively far from the nucleus, are held to the atom more weakly than the electrons which are in close to the nucleus. These outer electrons are frequently torn away. In the Crookes tube, the atom is battered about by a kind of electrical storm when a discharge passes through the gas in the tube. A collision with x-rays, ultraviolet rays, or a swiftly moving particle can jar loose an electron from an atom. High temperatures can also cause the loss of an electron. When a gas is sprayed through a fine nozzle, electrons can be rubbed off the atom. The loss of an electron from an atom is therefore a frequent event.

When one or more electrons are missing from an atom, there is a surplus of positive charge left over. The atom acquires a positive charge equal in size to the number of electrons lost. This process is called *ionization*, and the incomplete atom which now carries a charge is called an *ion*.

For the most part, the atoms on earth are complete and are not ions. The temperatures are too low for ionization to be produced by heat. In stars, where temperatures can be as high as millions of degrees, it is rare to find a whole atom. At these temperatures, the atoms are stripped of electrons. The stars are also filled with fast-moving particles, x-rays, and other radiation which attack atoms and tear away electrons.

On earth atoms are ionized at will in research laboratories. Physicists can produce x-rays, ultraviolet rays, extreme temperatures, a large number of fast particles, or even simple friction to supply ions as desired.

We may have oversimplified the picture of ionization. For example, in a tube like the Crookes tube, the situation can be very complicated. In the Crookes tube, the atmosphere contains three different kinds of particles. There are electrons donated by the metal of the cathode and electrons knocked off atoms of the gas. There are atoms of gas that are still intact and contain all their electrons. Then there are damaged atoms of the gas which have already lost one or more electrons. The electrons are negative, the whole atoms are neutral, and the damaged atoms are positive. The whole atoms are not affected by the voltage applied to the electrodes of the tube. The electrons and the ions tend to be separated by this voltage, the negative electrons moving toward the positive electrode (anode), the positive ions moving toward the negative electrode (cathode). However, all three are mixed together in the space inside the tube. Some of the whole atoms are in the process of being ionized. Some of the electrons come near ions as they travel past each other. The positive ions attract and swallow up the

320. An atom of oxygen. *A cluster of 8 protons and 8 neutrons forms the nucleus of an oxygen atom with a charge of +8 and a weight of 16. Eight electrons revolve in various orbits about the nucleus.*

354

THE OXYGEN ATOM

PROTONS

NEUTRONS

ELECTRONS

negative electrons. This recombination makes the ions whole atoms again and they become neutral, either to remain that way or to become ionized again before very long. Ions that have lost two electrons may capture only one and therefore remain ions, but with a smaller charge. The Crookes tube is indeed a battleground of atomic particles. Positive particles bombard the cathode and electrons are hurled against the glass and against the anode. The light that is produced is a means by which the gas in the tube or the glass of the tube relieves itself of some of the energy generated in the conflict.

The Atom Breaks the Law

The new picture of the atom explained many things observed in the laboratories. It was with great reluctance that physicists admitted the picture was wrong. At least, it could not be completely correct.

What was wrong was that the electrons revolving about the nucleus of an atom broke one of the laws of physics. According to this law, an electron moving in a circle must lose energy continually. A loss of energy would make it slow down gradually and spiral into the nucleus. But this does not happen. The scientists had to face the fact that the laws of motion did not apply to the inside of an atom. These laws were true enough for stars, planets, our own bodies, and the objects all about us, even down to whole atoms and molecules. However, inside the atom there seemed to be a new, unexplored world with strange laws of its own.

The physicists set out to explore and try to understand this new world, like tourists seeking to learn the customs of a strange land. In 1913, the Danish physicist Niels Bohr (figure 321) announced that he had succeeded in discovering some of the laws that governed the behavior of the atom. A German physicist by the name of Arnold Sommerfeld expanded Bohr's theory to make it fit the observed facts more accurately.

According to this theory, the secret of an electron's motion about a nucleus is that the electron is not free to travel any orbit it chooses. It is forced to move only in certain, special orbits. The Bohr-Sommerfeld theory explained how to calculate the allowed orbits. These orbits are like tracks laid down in closed loops about a common center, each track at a different distance from the center. The electrons are runners who must run on the tracks, never in between. It is possible for an electron to run sometimes on one track and other times on another track, but the ground between the tracks is forbidden territory.

Are the Electrons Really Planets?

What kind of a planetary system could the atom be, governed by the sort of rules children make up for silly games? This question touches on a problem that still faces modern scientists. It is a problem that concerns the difference between what is real and what is only a scientific theory invented to suit a particular set of observations.

Before the twentieth century, a scientist might feel that his theory described reality because it successfully fitted the results of his experiments. The gravitational force was real. Matter was real. Light waves were real. If the equations of his theory did not give exactly correct answers, a scientist might feel that his theory had faults. But he also felt that it dealt with real things and needed only a little patching up to be a true description of the real world. In the twentieth century we are no longer sure that we know what we mean by the real world. Instead, we make up models like the one we have just presented of the atom. We cannot say that our model is the real atom. We cannot say that electrons really whirl about the nucleus in certain paths. We cannot measure these paths the way astronomers measure the orbits of the heavenly planets. We merely say that, up to a certain point, it is useful to think of the atom as being similar to such a model. The electrons act *as if* they follow these orbits about the nucleus. The electrons act *as if* certain orbits are allowed and others are forbidden.

The small particles that inhabit the strange world we have uncovered are too small to be observed directly under a microscope. In many respects, they do not behave like the large bodies with which we are familiar. Therefore, we must be prepared to accept strange notions describing these particles, but we must accept these strange notions for what they are.

321. Niels Bohr (1885–1962). *Bohr, a Danish physicist, applied the new Quantum Theory to the Rutherford model of the atom. By proposing that electrons revolve about the atomic nucleus only in certain allowed orbits he was able to explain the colors emitted by an excited hydrogen atom as viewed through a spectroscope.*

They are artificial models that help us to organize our thoughts, to simplify masses of information that would otherwise be only separate, unrelated pieces. These models and the theories behind them sometimes make us feel uncomfortable, because they do not seem "real." We must recognize that they do not have to be "real" to be useful. We must judge them only by how successful they are. How successfully do they sum up our scientific findings? How successfully do they predict the results of experiments that we may perform?

Energy of Atomic Electrons In our model of the atom we do not have to worry because the electrons appear to travel only in certain selected orbits. It is enough that thinking of them in such a way helps to describe their behavior and leads to other useful discoveries. For example, a calculation of the separation between orbits involves a number that is also related to the separation of light into particles. It turns out that we find this same number wherever we find small particles like electrons or small distances like the spaces inside atoms.

To understand the significance of the different orbits of the electrons, we must understand the meaning of energy. This is because the most important property of an orbit is the energy possessed by the electron when it occupies that orbit. The electron has a different energy in each orbit.

What is energy? For once we have a word that means the same thing in physics that it means in everyday conversation.

Energy is the ability to do work. We meet energy in many familiar forms, such as heat, electricity, magnetism, and chemical energy. Sometimes energy is stored in one form but is changed into another form before being put to use. An electric battery contains chemicals which store energy in a chemical form. Yet, when the battery is connected to a flashlight bulb, the energy is converted to electricity. In the bulb the electrical energy is changed into heat energy and light energy. Energy has many forms, and the forms are interchangeable into each other. Two forms are of special interest in connection with the orbits of atomic electrons. One is energy possessed by a body because of its position, even though the body is sitting still. The other is energy possessed by a body because it is moving.

A flower pot sitting high on a window sill is capable of doing work. It can fall and smash itself or give an unlucky passer-by a crack on the head. This takes work. The peaceful pot, therefore, has energy because of its high position.

The flower pot has energy while sitting still. Water splashing against the blades of a waterwheel has energy because it is moving. It turns the wheel which may be connected to an electric generator from which electricity may flow to light and heat our homes. Wind can uproot trees and tear shingles from a roof. The air in the wind has energy because it is moving. Another example of the energy of motion is the falling flower pot.

The energy due to position is called

potential energy. The energy due to motion is called *kinetic energy*. When the flower pot falls from its perch, potential energy is converted into kinetic energy. The flower pot has potential energy in its high position because of the attraction of the earth. It is this attraction that makes the pot fall and enables it to do work. The higher the window sill, the more potential energy the flower pot contains and the more damage it can do when it falls. Let us see how this is similar to the situation inside the atom.

The electrons are attracted to the nucleus because they have opposite electric charges. The electrons would like to fall into the nucleus as the flower pot falls to the sidewalk, but inside the strange world of the atom the electrons are not permitted to do this. Since an electron must be in some orbit, and since only certain orbits are permitted, an electron can only fall from an orbit farther from the nucleus into an orbit which is closer. It can fall no farther than to the orbit closest to the nucleus. If our flower pot were subject to the same rules, it could sit only on certain window sills. It could not fall to the ground. It could fall only to the lowest permitted window sill.

An electron in an orbit far from the nucleus has more potential energy than an electron in an orbit nearer the nucleus. In our flower pot story, we saw that a pot on a higher sill had more potential energy than a pot on a lower sill. The reason is the same. But the electron is moving. Actually, it is not only sweeping around

the nucleus, it is also spinning like a top. Therefore, the electron also has kinetic energy while it is in an orbit. This is different from the flower pot, which sits still until it falls.

The total energy of an electron in an atom is the sum of its kinetic energy of motion plus the potential energy of its orbital position.

Energy Levels The image of electrons circling the nucleus of an atom in specific orbits was appealing because it was easy to visualize and, for a while at least, it fitted the known facts. It soon became apparent, however, that this simple picture did not completely explain the behavior of electrons in atoms. Up to a point, it was possible to overcome objections to the orbital model by proposing more complicated orbits. It was suggested that various orbits were circles while others were ellipses. An electron in a circular orbit has an energy that is slightly different from the energy of an electron in an elliptical orbit of the same average distance from the nucleus. This helped to explain why electrons in atoms could have energies close to each other yet clearly distinct. Other small differences were accounted for by supposing that two electrons might travel in the same orbit with one spinning with a right-hand screw motion and the other with a left-hand spin. But other, more subtle objections were raised which could not be explained away merely by adding complications to the orbital theory.

A more satisfactory representation of

electrons in atoms is by means of *energy levels*. The orbital model itself was invented to account for the particular energies found to be carried by the electrons. Since it is the energies that are of fundamental importance, the description of electronic orbits has given way to a listing of electronic energy levels. It is still sometimes useful to speak of orbits, especially in an elementary discussion, but we must be on guard against carrying the image too far.

The energy levels are not a disorderly scramble of numbers even if they cannot be easily associated with simple orbits. It has been found that the energy levels in an atom follow a simple numerical scheme. Each energy level is described by a set of four numbers called *quantum numbers*, like a man with four names. These numbers obey certain rules which enable the scientist to calculate how many energy levels can exist in a given atom.

The Exclusion Principle It was the German physicist Wolfgang Pauli who found one of the vital keys to the orderly arrangement of the electrons.

The energy levels are, in a sense, the permitted places where electrons may find a home. Imagine that these levels are seats in a theater. The doors open and electrons rush in to scramble for seats. What happens? The first ones in take the seats down front. These seats are the lowest energy levels. In the orbital model, these correspond to orbits closest to the nucleus. Latecomers find these front seats already oc-cupied and must look around in the rear. Finally all the seats are filled. If more electrons come into the theater, they are rejected, for there is no standing room allowed. They may replace an electron which leaves its seat. Otherwise they must drift on to another theater, that is, another atom.

Pauli stated the principle that one and only one electron could occupy a given energy level at any one time. Only one electron is permitted to fill a seat. Stated in other terms, no two electrons can have the same 4 quantum numbers in the same atom at the same time. This is called the *Pauli exclusion principle*.

With the exclusion principle and other information, it became possible to guess at how atoms might be built up and how the electronic arrangement in one atom is related to the arrangement in a different atom.

We can imagine a bare nucleus, stripped of all electrons. Now we permit electrons to enter one at a time, as if we were ushers in the atomic theater. In the atom of hydrogen, there is only 1 electron. The first electron therefore enters the lowest possible energy level and there is room for no more.

When the atom is one of helium, there is room for 2 electrons. The first electron enters an energy level very similar to that of the single electron in the hydrogen atom. The second electron enters the next higher energy level. In the orbital picture, these 2 electrons have the same orbit, but one has a right-hand spin and the other a left-hand spin. The helium atom is now filled.

The next atom is lithium with a charge of $+3$ on its nucleus and room for 3 electrons. The first 2 electrons fill the lowest 2 energy levels which are very much like the 2 energy levels of the helium electrons. If we carefully use the idea of orbits again we might say that the orbit closest to the nucleus cannot accept any more electrons. An electron can spin only two ways and the electrons in the innermost orbit have already used up these two possibilities. The third electron therefore enters an orbit more distant from the nucleus.

As we proceed to atoms with room for more and more electrons, beryllium with 4 electrons, boron with 5, carbon with 6, nitrogen with 7, and so on, we find that the picture becomes less simple. The second orbit proves to be a group of orbits, one circular, the others ellipses. Some ellipses are wider than others, but the number of possible ellipses is limited by the rules that govern the energy levels. For each ellipse there are a specific number of possible ways in which the magnetism surrounding the spinning electrons can contribute to the total energy of the electron. And for each of these the electron can be spinning to the right or to the left. Adding up all these possibilities, we find that there are 8 different energy states in the second group of orbits, that is, room for 8 electrons.

The atom of neon has 10 electrons. Two of these fill the first innermost group of energy levels. Eight fill the levels in the

322. Electron orbits in a xenon atom. *According to the Bohr-Sommerfeld model, electron orbits can be grouped into "shells" surrounding the nucleus. The 54 electrons of xenon occupy 5 shells in which 5_1 and 5_2 are two subgroups in the fifth shell, and 4_1, 4_2, and 4_3 are three subgroups in the fourth shell.*

second group of orbits. When we go on to the atom of sodium with 11 electrons, we find that the first 10 fill very much the same positions as the 10 electrons of neon. The last electron begins a new group which, in our orbital model, would correspond to an orbit still farther from the nucleus.

Electron Shells Still using the picture of atomic orbits, these groups of orbits are somewhat like concentric shells surrounding the nucleus like the layers of an onion. They are given the name *electron shells*. The first shell has room for 2 electrons, the second for 8, the third for 18, the fourth for 32, and the fifth for 50 electrons. The shells themselves could be called by the numbers 1, 2, 3, and so on, but for historical reasons are named by the letters *K, L, M, N,* and *O—K* being the innermost shell.

As we proceed from atom to atom with ever-increasing numbers of electrons, we find that the inner shells are gradually filled before the next outer shell begins to accept electrons. There are a few exceptions to this rule. In certain special cases, electrons enter a higher shell before the lower one is completely filled, but even this process follows certain rules.

We could play the game of putting electrons in their places all the way up to the element nobellium with 102 electrons and lawrencium with 103. However, to show how complex the representation can become, it is sufficient to show a diagram of the atom of xenon (figure 322). Xenon is a gas and its atoms contain 54 electrons. The numbers 5_1 and 5_2 refer to two little groups of electrons in the fifth shell. Similarly, 4_1, 4_2, and 4_3 refer to three little groups in the fourth shell. The little groups within a shell are called *subshells*. In the orbital model, the subshells correspond to the circles and ellipses that make up the orbital group.

As a final indication of how complex the atomic structure can be, it should be pointed out that the energy levels we described are not the only levels existing in the atom. They are merely the principal levels and determine the number of electrons within each shell grouping. Interactions between electrons or between the electrons and the nucleus, as well as dis-

turbances of the atom from the outside, cause departures from these principal levels. Therefore, the levels listed above give only the crude outlines of atomic structure and omit many of the fine details.

Chemistry and the Outside Electrons

Putting electrons in their proper place is not just a game like pinning the tail on the donkey. It turns out to be the foundation of all chemistry. Atoms that have similarities in the arrangement of their electrons also act in a similar way in chemical reactions. Let us see what is meant by a similarity in the arrangement of electrons.

First let us look at the atoms of elements that are known for their resistance to combining with other elements. They are called *stable* or *inert* elements. They remain unchanged even while other elements around them undergo chemical reaction. In this group of stable elements we find helium, neon, argon, krypton, xenon, and radon. What do they have in common? They are all gases. Because they are so stable, they are called the *noble gases*. But they have something else in common. They all have the right numbers of electrons to fill electron shells exactly with no electrons left over. Some do not fill the main shells, *K, L, M,* and so on, but they do fill subshells. Helium has 2 electrons which just fill the *K* shell. Neon has 10 electrons which just fill both the *K* and *L* shells. Argon has 18 electrons which just fill the *K* and *L* shells and the first two subshells of the *M* shell.

A shell or subshell that is filled is referred to as *closed*. It appears that a closed shell is like a protective wall around the atom, shielding it against chemical attack by other atoms. We might think of an atom as a little city that is forever being invaded by enemy atoms. The electron shells are the city walls that keep out the enemy. If the shells are complete, the walls are strong and the atom is stable. But if there are not enough electrons in the atom to complete the outer shell or subshell, the wall has a gap in it and is weak. The atom can be attacked by other atoms and take part in a chemical reaction. Also, if an outer shell is completed, but there are one or more electrons left over, these extra electrons must occupy the next unfilled shell where they are relatively unprotected. Such atoms are also chemically active.

In fact, we find that the chemical properties of atoms depend on whether their electrons just fill electron shells, whether the number of electrons is just short of filling a shell, or whether there are a few electrons left over after a shell is filled. Atoms that have 1 electron left over are said to have 1 electron in the outermost unfilled shell. Hydrogen is one of these. It has only 1 electron. There are no filled shells. Therefore, there is just 1 electron drifting about in the outer regions of the atoms. Lithium is the next atom in this condition. It has 3 electrons. Two fill the K shell, the innermost group of orbits, and again there is just 1 electron in the outermost unfilled shell. The next such atom is

323. Dmitri Ivanovich Mendeleev (1834–1907). *This famous Russian chemist was the author of the Periodic Table of the Elements, which showed the relationship between atomic weights and chemical properties of elements. The position of gaps in his table enabled him to predict the properties of elements previously undiscovered.*

sodium with 11 electrons. Two electrons fill and close off the K shell, 8 fill and close off the L shell, and again there is 1 electron left over outside the last closed shell. If we study the chemical properties of hydrogen, lithium, and sodium, we find that they have many similarities. Lithium, sodium, potassium, and the other metals found in this group are given the name of *alkali metals* because their chemical properties are so much alike.

If we make up a list of elements whose

atoms have 2 electrons left over after a shell or subshell is closed, we find that they, too, behave very much like each other. However, they are different from the alkali metals listed above. In general, it is true that elements with atoms that have the same number of electrons in outer unfilled shells also have chemical properties that are similar to each other.

A Remarkable Confirmation This relation between chemical properties and the planetary electrons in the atom is a remarkable confirmation of a discovery that was made long ago. Many men had noticed that some elements resembled others in their chemical behavior. They suspected that there was some system that could account for this, and they tried listing the elements in various ways on charts to find the key to the mystery.

At a time when nothing was known of electrons and electron shells, a successful chart was made up which arranged the elements in a simple order according to their atomic weights. This was the *periodic table* composed by the Russian chemist Dmitri Ivanovich Mendeleev (figure 323) in 1868. He wrote down the elements in rows in the order of increasing atomic weight. First came hydrogen, the lightest of all, then helium, lithium, and so on, all the way down to uranium, then the heaviest. He also spaced the names of the elements so that those with similar chemical properties were lined up one under the other in vertical columns. Such an arrangement of the elements is shown in the comprehensive table in figure 324.

Mendeleev did not have all the elements at his disposal because some of them had not yet been discovered. Therefore, his table had gaps in it where he had to allow space for the unknown elements. When the nature of the atoms and the electrons in them was discovered, it became clear that it was not the atomic weights that were of first importance, but the atomic numbers. Remember that the atomic number is the number of electrons in the atom. This is also equal to the charge on the nucleus. Once this was known, the elements could be listed in order of increasing atomic number. Atomic weights sometimes have strange numbers. Hydrogen has an atomic weight of 1 which is simple enough. The next element, helium, has an atomic weight of 4. But after that come lithium with an atomic weight of 6.94, beryllium with 9.02, boron with 10.82, and so on. These are not whole numbers and they do not go up in simple steps. The atomic numbers rise in simple steps of 1, 1 electron for hydrogen, 2 electrons for helium, 3 for lithium, 4 for beryllium, 5 for boron, and so on.

The numbers should proceed from 1 for hydrogen to 103 for lawrencium. Missing numbers stand out like missing teeth. These missing numbers gave chemists good clues which helped them to discover the missing elements and fill in all the spaces.

In the table in figure 324, elements are listed with their atomic numbers.

Mendeleev arrived at the periodic table by hard work, trial and error, and intelligent guesses. It agreed beautifully with the model of the atom that resulted from the brilliant efforts of Rutherford, Bohr, and Sommerfeld.

Electron Jumps The confirmation of the periodic table was not the only success enjoyed by the new model of the atom. It also led to an explanation of the light that is given off by the gases in a Crookes tube or neon sign. It showed why each had the particular colors it displayed. Moreover, it uncovered the source of the mysterious radiation called x-rays. Our story of how this came about will begin with a closer study of the electrons and how they move about the nucleus.

Let us begin with the simplest atom of all, hydrogen with its single electron. If there is no interference from the outside, the electron in the hydrogen atom rotates about the nucleus in the orbit that is closest to the nucleus. It will remain there forever.

Now let us somehow give the electron a kick. We can do this by hitting the electron with a ray of light or by shooting at it with a fast-moving particle which might be an atom or even another electron. The electron of the hydrogen atom is knocked out of its innermost orbit. If the kick is gentle, the electron will jump to the second orbit. It is still permitted to travel only in the prescribed orbits, never in between. In the second orbit, the electron has more energy. To knock the electron from the first to the second orbit, the kick must supply the electron with enough energy to make up the difference. If the kick is too gentle, the electron cannot jump all the way to the second orbit and will remain in the first. If the kick is harder, more energy is given the electron and it may even jump out to the third or fourth orbit, skipping the ones in between. If the kick is hard enough, the electron will be thrown out of the atom completely. This atom with a missing electron will become a hydrogen ion. Instead of being electrically neutral, it will acquire a charge of $+1$.

Let us suppose that the electron is kicked into a higher orbit, but not out of the atom altogether. The higher orbits are not safe, comfortable positions. They are like narrow ledges in the side of a steep cliff. In a short time the electron tumbles from the ledge to fall back toward the more secure first orbit, safely close to the nucleus. However, the electron may not always fall directly into the first orbit again. It often falls first to some intermediate orbit, then to another, then to another, always downward, until finally it does reach the first orbit. It is a little like a ball bouncing down stairs. It may bounce on each step, may skip some steps, or it may even bounce from a high step straight to the bottom.

Between any two orbits there is a very definite difference in energy. When the electron is kicked from one orbit to a higher orbit, it gains from the kick exactly this amount of energy, no more and no less. When it falls back from a higher orbit to a lower orbit, it must give up energy. The amount of energy it gives up

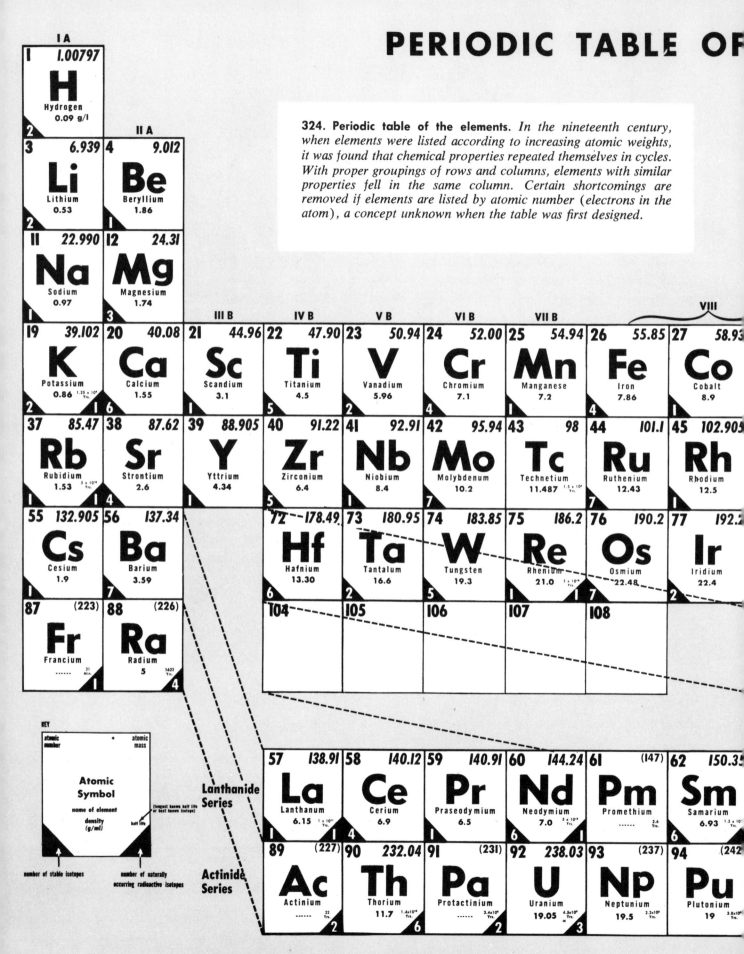

324. Periodic table of the elements. *In the nineteenth century, when elements were listed according to increasing atomic weights, it was found that chemical properties repeated themselves in cycles. With proper groupings of rows and columns, elements with similar properties fell in the same column. Certain shortcomings are removed if elements are listed by atomic number (electrons in the atom), a concept unknown when the table was first designed.*

HE ELEMENTS

BASED ON CARBON-12

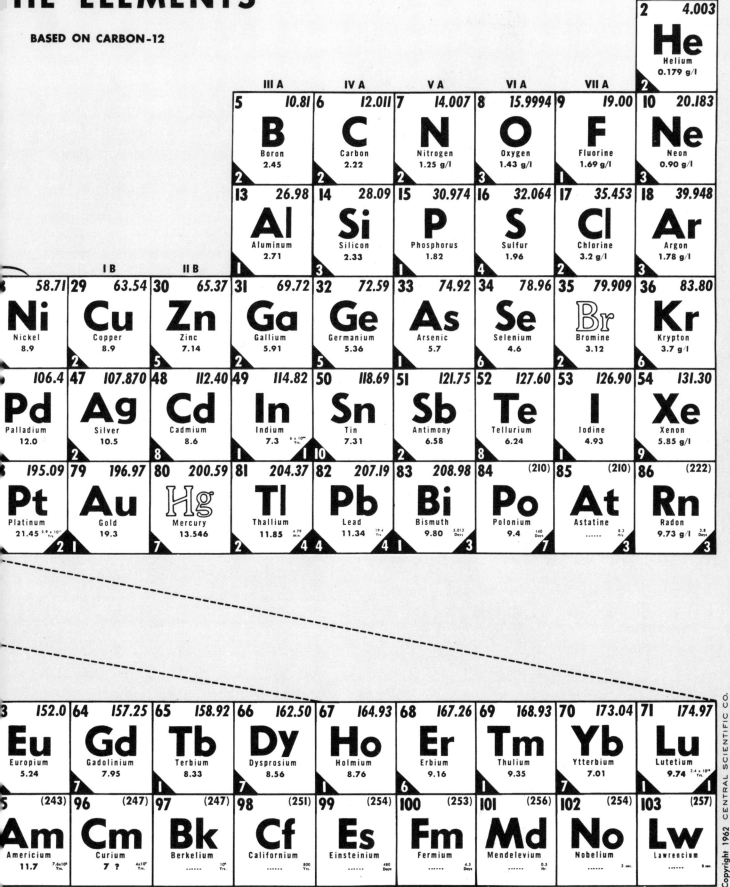

325. Max Planck (1858–1947). *Planck's Quantum Theory revolutionized physics and won him the Nobel Prize in 1918. To explain the wave lengths of light radiated from hot bodies (related to colors when the light is visible), the German physicist proposed that energy was emitted in little packets called quanta, rather than in a continuous stream.*

is exactly equal to the difference in energy between the two orbits, again no more and no less. The farther apart the two orbits are, the more energy must be gained or lost. The closer the two orbits are, the less energy must be gained or lost in the electron jump.

When an electron is kicked to a very high orbit, a hard kick is required and the electron gains a large amount of energy. When it falls again, it may fall in little bounces from orbit to orbit, giving up little bursts of energy with each bounce. If it falls straight down to the first orbit, it gives up all the energy difference in one large burst.

Since the difference in energy between orbits is a very specific number, it is given a special name. It is called a *quantum* of energy. As you can tell from the sound of the word, a quantum is a definite quantity of energy.

To present as simple a picture as possible, we have described the electron as jumping from one orbit to another. Actually, it is better to think of the electron as passing from one energy level in one electron shell to another energy level in another electron shell. The jump is always from one shell to another. But within each shell there are a number of energy levels. Therefore the exact difference in energy across which the electron jumps depends on the particular level it leaves in one shell and the particular level it enters in the other shell.

What Is a Quantum? The idea of the quantum represents one of the great discoveries of modern physics. Energy does not come from the atom in a continuous stream. It is made up of little bits or *quanta* (plural of quantum). A quantum is like an atom of energy, except that a quantum truly cannot be divided into smaller parts. We may have a small quantum or a large quantum, 2 quanta or 100 quanta, but never half a quantum or a quarter of a quantum.

When an electron jumps between orbits that are close to each other, the quantum of energy gained or lost is a small one. When the orbits are far from each other, the quantum is a large one.

Electron jumps are not peculiar to the hydrogen atom. All the atoms behave the same way. The more electrons the atoms have, the more complicated the situation becomes. When there are many orbits between which to jump, and many electrons to jump about, there can be many different sizes of quanta taken up or given out by the electron jumps. The orbits in different atoms correspond to different energies. This is expected since the energy in an orbit is largely determined by the force of attraction pulling the electron toward the nucleus. When the electrical charge on the nucleus is larger, as it is for elements with high atomic numbers, the forces can be greater.

Thus, we have a very complicated situation with electrons leaping about from orbit to orbit when excited by the addition of energy from outside the atom. We also have the key to an understanding of the situation in our model of the atom. No matter how complicated the atom, if we have enough patience, we can analyze the mixture of quanta given up or taken in. From these numbers, we can actually separate the various orbits and energy levels that exist in a given atom. We can then compare these with orbits calculated mathematically from our assumed picture of

the very intricate structure of the atom.

The question then is, how can we find these quanta to study them and measure them? The answer lies in the way a quantum is emitted by an atom when an electron makes a jump from a higher to a lower orbit.

Light and X-rays A quantum of energy is emitted by an atom in the form of electromagnetic radiation, such as a little bundle of light. The energy in each bundle of light is exactly equal to the energy in a single quantum. You may recall that there was once a dispute as to whether light was a simple wave or a stream of particles. We stated that the modern theory accepts the fact that light is both. Light is a group of waves that travel along in such a way that they become knotted up into separate little bundles. Each little bundle is a quantum of light, also called a *photon*. (*Photos* is the Greek word for light and is the origin of words such as photograph, photostat, and photoengraving.) But what does a quantum of light tell us about the light?

It was discovered that the frequency of the light is simply proportional to the energy in a quantum of the light. Since the frequency is also related to the color of the light, the size of the quantum determines the color. The discovery of this principle by the German physicist Max Planck won him the Nobel Prize in physics in 1918. Planck invented the quantum and developed the *quantum theory,* the basis for much of modern physics.

Atoms emit quanta of many different sizes. The difference in energy between two orbits determines the quantum of energy emitted when an electron jumps between the two. When the orbits are close to the nucleus, the difference in energy between one orbit and the next is large. When the orbits are far from the nucleus, the difference in energy between consecutive orbits is much smaller. Therefore, when an electron falls from some higher orbit to one close to the nucleus, it must jump a wide gap and the quantum emitted is large. The frequency of the light that appears is therefore high. The frequency may be so high that our eyes cannot see the light. The light may be ultraviolet or even higher in frequency, as we shall see later. When the electron jump is between orbits that are far from the nucleus, the quantum emitted will be smaller. The frequency of the resulting light will be lower, and we will be able to see it as red, yellow, green, violet, or some other color.

Remember that energy is emitted only when electrons are falling back from orbits of higher energy to orbits of lower energy. To produce light, the electrons must first be kicked up to higher orbits.

In even a small amount of material there are many billions of atoms. In each atom the electrons are jumping about when excited by an electrical discharge, bombardment by light rays, ultraviolet rays, or swift particles. There are electrons jumping between all possible combinations of orbits and many electron jumps may be taking place at the same time. The energy com-

ing out of the large group of atoms therefore contains quanta of many different sizes all at the same time. With the aid of the spectroscope, which we described earlier, we can separate the quanta of different sizes according to the frequency of the light they produce. By measuring the frequency of each group, we can calculate the energy in each of the quanta. In this way, we can actually trace them back to the orbits in the atom.

Now let us return to the kind of light produced when the quanta are very large compared with the quanta of visible light. These quanta come from electron jumps to orbits closer to the nucleus where there are greater differences in energy between orbits. These large quanta are the *x-rays* which have such high frequencies that they can penetrate our bodies and disclose the bones beneath our flesh.

Back to the Crookes Tube Once More We will make one last visit to the Crookes tube to show a practical example of what we have been talking about. We have a sealed glass tube with a metal cathode at one end and a metal anode at the other end. We place a high voltage between the two with the anode positive and the cathode negative. Electrons, which are

326. X-ray photograph of a child's chest. *Soon after their discovery by Roentgen in 1895, and years before they were understood, x-rays were put to use in medical research and diagnosis. Today there is a greater awareness of the harm they can do, and x-rays are applied with caution under carefully controlled conditions.*

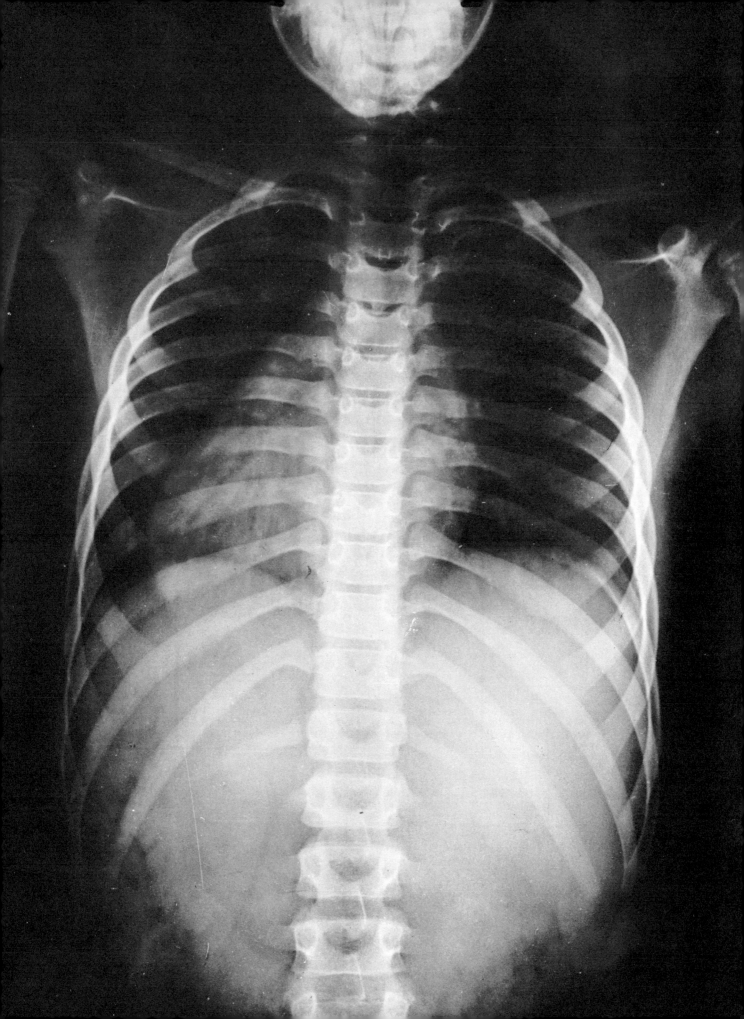

negative, are emitted by the cathode. These electrons are drawn to the anode because of its positive charge. If there were a perfect vacuum in the tube, that is, no gas at all, the space would be absolutely clear and the electrons would rush at great speed directly from the cathode toward the anode. Let us come back to such a condition later. At present, let us assume that there is a certain pressure of gas in the tube.

The electrons start to race from the cathode toward the anode. They find in their path a cloud of gas atoms, perhaps tied together in pairs to form molecules. There are so many gas atoms that the electrons bump into them almost immediately. When an electron hits an atom it gives one of the atomic electrons a kick into a higher orbit. The onrushing electron loses some of its energy. This energy is gained by the atomic electron, permitting it to rotate in its new orbit of higher energy. The cathode electron is slowed down, but not stopped. It goes on to collide with another atom, then another and another. Each collision causes an electron in the atom struck to rise to a higher energy orbit. Some collisions are violent enough to knock electrons completely out of gas atoms. These atoms become ionized. When a cathode electron, tired from a number of collisions, comes near an ionized gas atom, which is missing one or even more electrons, the electron is gobbled up by the atom.

Meanwhile, in atoms in which planetary electrons have been driven to higher energy orbits, these electrons begin to tumble back to the lower orbits. In doing so, they give up the energy they gained during the earlier collision. This energy is emitted by the atcm as a quantum of light. The scene of the clashes between electrons racing from the cathode and the gas atoms blocking their path becomes a volume of glowing gas. The glow is made up of colors whose frequency depends on the size of the quanta being emitted. These, in turn, depend on the differences in energy between the orbits in the gas atoms among which the planetary electrons are jumping up and falling down.

Now let us pump out most of the gas. There are still some gas atoms to be struck by the electrons coming from the cathode. Hence, there is still a glowing light emitted by the gas. However, the gas atoms are fewer and farther apart. Electrons can travel farther before they collide with a gas atom. Some of them even manage to reach the glass walls. Here they smash against the glass and excite the atoms of the glass. This causes the atoms of the glass to emit light. The color of this light now depends on the structure of the atoms in the glass.

The less gas there is in the tube, the more electrons can hit the glass walls on their way toward the anode. The electrons can also hit harder because they have not lost some of their energy in earlier collisions. As a result, more and more of the glass glows as we pump out more and more gas atoms.

The glass walls give off not only visible light but also x-rays. Why? The answer lies in the violence of the collisions between the cathode electrons and the glass. With the gas atoms removed, the electrons travel farther and pick up speed on the way. When they hit the glass, they are moving faster and hit harder than when they hit the gas atoms. They hit the glass so hard that they knock electrons out of the innermost orbits near the nucleus. Electrons in orbits farther from the nucleus immediately fall into the newly emptied inner orbits. This is a long drop and causes the emission of very energetic quanta. These are the quanta of x-rays.

We have now touched the heart of the mystery of light and x-rays. We know where they come from and how they are made. Infrared rays, visible light, ultraviolet light, and x-rays are all members of the same family. They differ only in the length of the jump made by the electrons which produce them. A tiny jump produces infrared, a larger jump visible light, a still larger jump ultraviolet, and a giant step emits x-rays.

Gamma Rays and Radio Waves In searching through the world of the atom, with its whirling electrons and strange rules and regulations, we unexpectedly came upon the source of light. At least, we found that electromagnetic radiation originates from the infrared frequencies to those of x-rays. We learned earlier that the family of electromagnetic radiations does not end here. Below infrared there are *radio waves,* and above the x-rays there are *gamma rays.* We did not mention these forms of radiation in connection with the energy jumps of atomic electrons because radio waves and gamma rays are born in different ways.

Radio waves are generated in an antenna at a broadcasting station or other transmitter. An *antenna* is a metal rod or wire in which an electric current races back and forth, back and forth, many times in a second. We have seen that an electric current is a flow of electrons. It is a flow of electrons which are not strongly attached to any atoms and therefore are free to flow in a wire like water in a pipe. Radio waves are therefore also the product of moving electrons. These electrons, however, are free. They are not atomic slaves, bound to move only in certain restricted orbits.

Gamma rays are similar to light rays and x-rays in their origin because they, too, are born from energy jumps. The jumps are not made by planetary electrons. Instead, they are made inside the nucleus of the atom itself.

The little atom can no longer be counted as a stranger to us. We have learned something of its structure, its laws, and the radiations it produces. We are well enough acquainted with the atom to venture more deeply into it and look more closely at its inner core, the nucleus.

The Atomic Nucleus and Its Elementary Particles

The Atomic Nucleus We plunge into the atom, brushing the whizzing electrons aside like a cloud of insects. The bare nucleus stands before us. In some ways it is a little disappointing. Although almost the entire mass of the atom is packed into it, the nucleus is only as big as one of the electrons we left behind. The nuclei of the atoms of different elements do not all have the same diameter, but they are all close to 10^{-13} inches. Some 10 million million of them could be lined up in an inch. In spite of their being approximately the same size, a nucleus weighs thousands of times as much as an electron.

The diameter of the whole atom is about 10^{-8} inches. Only 100 million atoms, more or less, can fit into an inch of length. The whole atom is therefore about 100,000 times the size of an electron or a nucleus. If we imagine the atom to be a ball a mile wide, the nucleus or one of the electrons is only a little bit bigger than one-half an inch. Most of the atom is empty space.

In other ways, however, the nucleus is quite impressive. With so much matter crammed into such a small space, the nucleus has an almost incredibly high density. Also, in this little space of one ten-million millionth of an inch there is another complex world, even stranger than the planetary system we discovered when we first met the atom. In this nuclear world there are inhabitants that are different from those in the atomic world. The nucleus also has its own code of laws which governs the motions and energies of the particles that dwell there.

In our discussion of the nucleus we will reach the limit of our present scientific knowledge. Much of the nuclear world is still hidden. Physicists at this moment are building machines that cover acres of ground in order to probe more deeply into the secrets of this unimaginably tiny dot of matter.

How do we go about penetrating the nucleus to find out what lies inside? The means we used before were chemical or physical. Heating, evaporating, filtering, dissolving, grinding, or mixing with other chemicals succeeded only in separating substances into the molecules or atoms of which they were built. We were like children separating toy blocks that had become glued together. Electrical discharges or bombardment of atoms with rays or particles managed to remove electrons from the atom, but they left the nucleus intact. The nucleus is a harder nut to crack.

The charge on the nucleus is what determines whether an atom is gold or silver, hydrogen or oxygen, lead or uranium. When we remove electrons or put them back, we are only playing with electricity. We are not changing gold into silver or hydrogen into oxygen. When we break a nucleus in two to examine its contents, we end up with 2 nuclei, each with a smaller mass and charge than the original. These are the nuclei of two other elements. This is truly like changing gold into silver, or lead into gold. Before man was able to do this in the laboratory, nature luckily came to his aid. Elements were found whose nuclei changed from one kind to another by themselves without outside help. This discovery was the beginning of our understanding of the nucleus.

327. Pierre Curie (1859–1906). *Already a well-known scientist for his work with crystals and magnetism, Curie joined his wife, Marie Curie, in her exciting research into new radioactive substances. Together they discovered the radioactive elements polonium and radium, for which they shared the Nobel Prize in physics in 1903 with Henri Becquerel, the discoverer of radioactivity.*

328. Marie Sklodowska Curie (1867–1934). *Madame Curie, one of the foremost woman scientists of our time, was a brilliant chemist and untiring laboratory worker. She not only shared one Nobel Prize for discoveries of radioactive elements with her husband, but was awarded a second prize in 1911 for the isolation of metallic radium.*

375

Natural Radioactivity The spontaneous transformation of the nucleus of one element into the nucleus of another element was discovered by the French physicist Henri Becquerel in March, 1896. For this he was awarded the Nobel Prize in physics. This transformation is called *natural radioactivity*. Becquerel's research was carried forward brilliantly by Pierre and Marie Curie (figures 327 and 328). In fact, Marie Curie is one of the rare people to receive two Nobel Prizes. Her prizes were in physics and in chemistry.

What is natural radioactivity? The word *radioactivity* means activity that results in radiations. It is found that certain chemical elements have nuclei that are unstable. They do not remain the same forever. The activity in radioactivity is the disintegration or breaking down of an unstable nucleus to form the nucleus of another kind of atom. In the process energy is given off in the form of rays that shoot out of the disintegrating nucleus. These are the radiations that result from the activity.

There is no way of predicting when a nucleus will break down. It may wait hundreds, thousands, or even billions of years before it suddenly erupts. However, there are so many atoms in even a small amount of radioactive material that there are always a number of nuclei in the process of erupting.

The first of these naturally occurring radioactive elements discovered was radium, with an atomic weight of 226 and a charge on its nucleus of $+88$. When a radium nucleus disintegrates, it suddenly shoots out part of itself, reducing its mass to 222 and its charge to $+86$. This is the nucleus of a completely different atom, that of the element called radon. The disintegration changes radium, a bright white metal, into radon, a gas. To do this, radium loses 4 units of mass and 2 units of charge. These are carried away by the ray that is shot out. This particular ray is called the *alpha ray*.

Alpha and Beta Rays Radioactive nuclei emit three different kinds of rays, called alpha, beta, and gamma after the first three letters of the Greek alphabet (the word alphabet is named after the first two letters). One or more of these rays appears with each disintegration. We will examine the alpha and beta rays first.

The *alpha ray* emitted by the radium nucleus when it decays is actually a particle of matter with a mass of 4 and a charge of $+2$. If we look at a list of atomic nuclei, we find that these are exactly the mass and charge of the nucleus of the helium atom. An alpha ray is just that, the nucleus of the helium atom with the two planetary electrons removed. The disintegration of a radium nucleus is really a split into a nucleus of radon and a nucleus of helium. The alpha ray, or helium nucleus, can easily capture two electrons from the surrounding air. It then becomes an ordinary atom of helium, no different from any other atom of helium with a less exciting history.

Another type of ray emitted by some radioactive substances is the *beta ray*. This

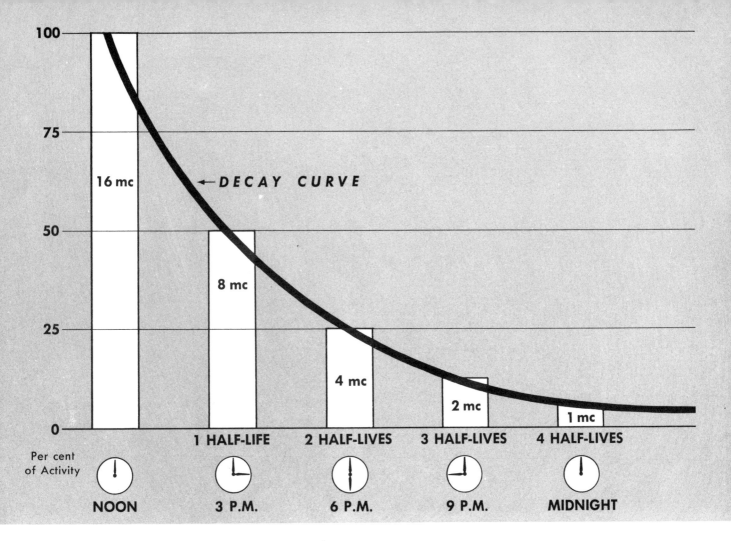

329. Meaning of half-life. *After a radioactive atom emits a ray, it no longer belongs to the group still capable of emitting that ray. The remaining atoms grow fewer with each emission. The activity,* *measured in millicuries (mc), is said to decay. Half-life is the length of time it takes, on the average, for half the atoms we start with to emit their rays. The chart represents a half-life of 3 hours.*

turns out to be nothing more than a fast-moving electron. When a decaying nucleus emits a beta particle, it loses almost none of its mass or weight because an electron has so little. However, the electron does carry an electric charge of -1. When a nucleus loses a charge of -1, it is the same as gaining a charge of $+1$. Therefore, when a beta ray is emitted, a new nucleus is formed with almost the same mass as before, but with a charge increased by one unit. This is all that is needed to change one chemical element into another. With the later discovery of artificial radioac-

tivity, it was found that beta rays could also have a positive charge. The positive electron is called a *positron*.

Alpha and beta rays are both particles, but the alpha particle is much heavier and has a double positive charge, whereas the beta particle is very light and has a single negative charge. There is another difference. An alpha particle is emitted from a particular nucleus with a very definite speed. This speed is different for alpha particles from different kinds of nuclei, but for alpha particles from the same kind of nuclei the speed is almost exactly the

RADIOACTIVITY OF CARBON—14

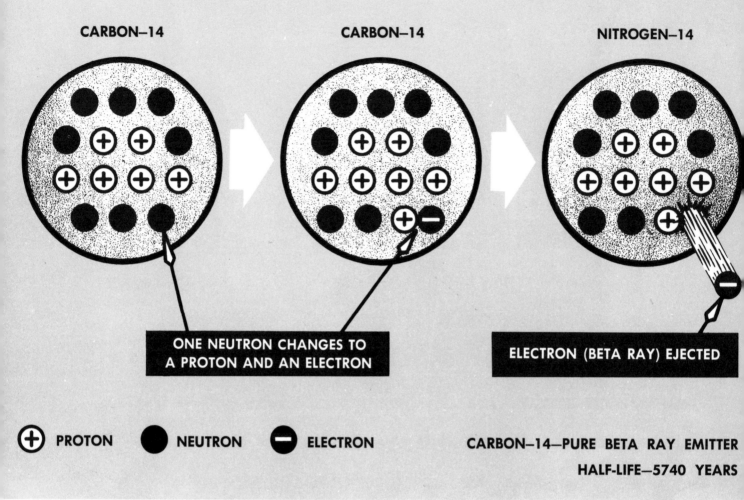

CARBON—14   CARBON—14   NITROGEN—14

ONE NEUTRON CHANGES TO
A PROTON AND AN ELECTRON

ELECTRON (BETA RAY) EJECTED

⊕ PROTON   ● NEUTRON   ⊖ ELECTRON

CARBON—14—PURE BETA RAY EMITTER
HALF-LIFE—5740 YEARS

330. Beta-ray emission. *A beta ray is an electron emitted by a nucleus, although theory states that a nucleus cannot contain an electron. The answer to the riddle is that the electron is created at the instant of emission. A carbon–14 nucleus contains 6 protons and 8 neutrons. One neutron changes to a proton and an electron just before the electron is emitted. In a positive beta-ray emitter, a proton changes to a neutron and a positron.*

same each time. Such speeds are of the order of 7500 to 12,500 miles a second.

The electrons which make up beta rays, on the other hand, may be quite slow or very fast, even when emitted from the same kind of nucleus. Beta rays from different kinds of nuclei are different only in the top speed that may be reached. The

top speed of beta rays from some nuclei comes very close to the speed of light (186,000 miles a second).

We can demonstrate the difference in charge between alpha and beta rays by a little experiment (figure 331). We place some radioactive material that emits all kinds of rays deep in a hole in a lead block. Only the rays that travel straight upward can find their way out of the hole. All the others are trapped by the lead. The rays that come out of the hole are passed between two metal plates to which we connect an electric battery. The right-hand plate is made electrically positive, the left-hand plate negative. We find that the positive alpha rays are attracted to the negative plate and their paths bend to the left. The negative beta rays (electrons) are attracted to the positive plate and their paths bend to the right. The third group of rays, the remaining gamma rays, do not bend at all. We know from this that they do not have an electric charge. What else do we know about gamma rays?

Gamma Rays Gamma rays cannot carry a charge because they are not particles. They are still another member of the family of electromagnetic radiations like radio waves, infrared, visible light, ultraviolet light, and x-rays. The gamma rays have the highest frequencies of all. They may be considered very short-wave x-rays.

Since the gamma rays are electromagnetic radiations, they always travel with the speed of light. When a nucleus emits a gamma ray, it loses almost no mass at all and no charge. What, then, is the part that the gamma ray plays in radioactivity? The loss of a gamma ray does not change a nucleus into the nucleus of another element. The answer to this question lies in the condition of a nucleus after it emits an alpha ray or a beta ray.

The emission of an alpha ray or a beta ray is an exciting event in the life of a nucleus. When the process is over, the newly formed nucleus usually finds itself in a highly nervous state. It is agitated with excess energy. To calm itself down to a normal existence, it rids itself of this energy by emitting a gamma ray. Very roughly, this is what happens during a radioactive transformation.

The Trail Left by Alpha, Beta, and Gamma Rays Alpha, beta, and gamma rays speed

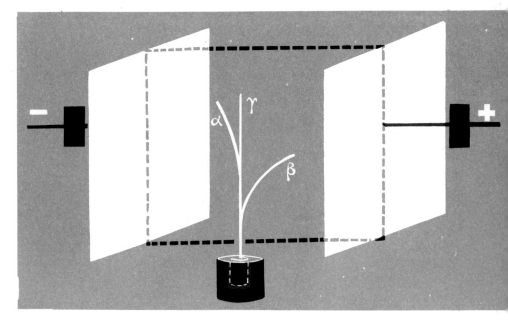

331. Separation of radioactive rays in an electric field. *The electric charges on the metal plates create an electric field which acts on charges between the plates. A positive α (alpha) ray is attracted to the negative plate, a negative β (beta) ray to the positive plate. An uncharged γ (gamma) ray passes undisturbed. A positive beta ray, emitted by artificially radioactive atoms, would also be drawn toward the negative plate like the alpha ray.*

332. Measuring energy levels of atomic nuclei.
Just as light results from "jumps" between energy levels by atomic electrons, so gamma rays are emitted by jumps between energy levels in the nucleus. Gamma rays cause scintillations (light pulses) when they strike certain crystals. Here the scintillations are being converted by a photoelectric tube into wedge-shaped pulses on an oscilloscope screen (like a TV picture tube). Wedge heights represent gamma-ray energies.

333. Alpha particles emitted in a nuclear collision.
A high-speed calcium nucleus struck a carbon atom in a photographic emulsion. Under the microscope, the developed film shows the long, unswerving track of this hit-and-run calcium nucleus. The shaken carbon nucleus disintegrated and emitted three alpha particles whose paths formed a three-pronged star, centered at the point of collision.

20μ

along with so much energy that they are capable of knocking electrons from atoms with which they collide. This leaves the atoms ionized and carrying a positive electric charge. Therefore, when the rays pass through a gas, they leave behind a trail of ionized gas atoms. The trail has a different character for each of the three types of rays.

An alpha particle is so big and heavy—7000 times heavier than a beta particle—that it simply plows a straight path through the gas. It brushes the gas atoms aside like a rocket hurtling through a cloud of ping-pong balls. The path is a scene of destruction littered with great quantities of ionized gas atoms. However, each collision takes its toll and gradually slows down the alpha particle. After many collisions, the alpha particle loses much of its energy and eventually is stopped.

The beta particle also leaves behind a trail of ionized gas atoms. However, it is so light in weight that it suffers more than the alpha particle from each collision with a gas atom. The beta particle does not move straight ahead but is forever bouncing to one side or another. Its path is a series of zigzags and curls. When its energy has been drained by too many collisions, the beta particle is in danger of being captured by an ionized atom seeking to regain a lost electron.

The alpha and beta particles leave a clear trail behind them like a bicycle on a muddy road. The gamma ray, however, slips between the atoms of gas and travels a much greater distance between collisions than do the other two rays. It also loses more of its energy in each collision and is completely exhausted after very few impacts. We do not see the path of the gamma ray between collisions. We see only the results of the infrequent impacts. Usually, most of these collisions are between a gamma ray and a planetary electron in a gas atom. The gamma ray loses so much energy, which is picked up by the electron, that the electron tears away from the atom and plunges into the surrounding gas as if it were a fast-moving beta ray. It is this particle, not the gamma ray that struck it, which produces the curved path of ionization in the gas. The passage of a stream of gamma rays through a gas is therefore marked by the small, curving trails of ionized gas atoms caused by the particles kicked out of atoms by occasional collisions with gamma rays.

The Cloud Chamber We spoke before as if we could really see the trails of ionized gas atoms left behind by the alpha, beta, and gamma rays. Fortunately, we are able to do almost exactly that. The instrument that permits us to see the paths of ionizing particles and radiations is called a *Wilson cloud chamber,* named for the man who invented it, C. T. R. Wilson. The cloud chamber makes ingenious use of the behavior of water vapor in air. Let us examine this behavior.

When water evaporates, molecules of water leave the liquid to hover about in the air. The molecules mixed with the air are called *water vapor.* At any given tem-

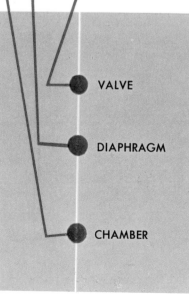

334. Wilson cloud chamber.

Named after its developer, C.T.R. Wilson, a British physicist, the cloud chamber makes visible the path of an ionizing ray. The chamber contains a gas and a saturated vapor of water or alcohol. Operation of the valve pulls the flexible diaphragm down, suddenly expanding the chamber and cooling the vapor. This causes droplets of dew to form on the gas particles electrified by the passage of the ray.

VALVE

DIAPHRAGM

CHAMBER

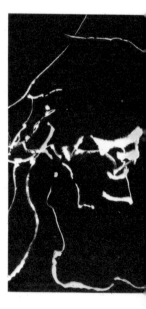

Tracks of radioactive rays in a cloud chamber.

335. Alpha rays. *Fast, heavy alpha particles plunge straight through the gas, undeflected by collisions with gas molecules while creating ions in abundance.*

336. Gamma rays. *The path of the gamma-ray beam is straight from left to right, but electrons knocked out of gas atoms by the rays trace meandering tracks like those of beta particles.*

337. Beta rays. *Lightweight beta particles (electrons) bounce off the gas molecules, changing course with each collision in zigzag, curving paths, and producing fewer ions than alpha rays.*

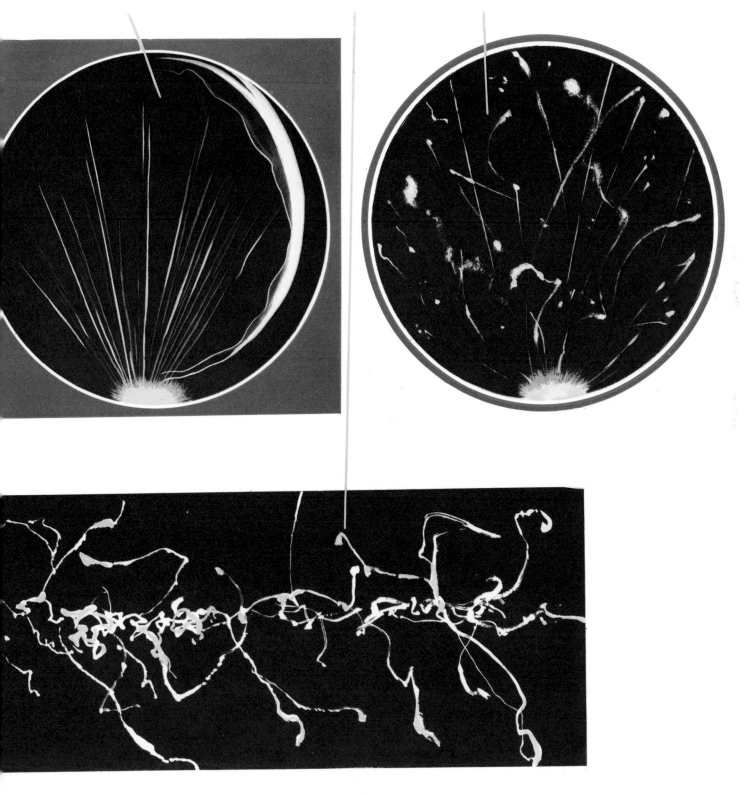

perature, the air can hold only a certain maximum amount of water vapor. When the air contains this amount of vapor, the air is said to be *saturated*. If we try to add more vapor, we find that some of the vapor already present condenses into water droplets. The air must give up some of its vapor in order to receive more.

Another way to cause the water vapor in the air to condense into droplets is to reduce the temperature. At a lower temperature, the air can hold less water vapor. If the air contains as much vapor as it can hold at a higher temperature, it will have more than it can hold at the new, lower temperature. This is why droplets of dew form on the grass on a cool night. It is found, however, that sometimes the droplets do not form when the temperature is lowered. The air is then said to be *supersaturated*. To help the droplets form, little grains of dust must be present around which the water molecules can collect. It was found that ionized gas atoms acted like the grains of dust, whereas neutral gas atoms did not promote the formation of water droplets.

Water droplets hanging in the air near the ground are called fog. High in the sky, sometimes frozen into ice crystals, they are called clouds. The main point is that fog and clouds are visible, whereas vapor molecules are not.

One more point must be made before we return to the Wilson cloud chamber. It is a well-known principle in physics that we can lower the temperature of a gas by causing it to expand suddenly. This prin-

ciple is applied in home refrigerators where a gas is compressed so much it becomes a liquid. When the pressure is suddenly removed the liquid is permitted to become a rapidly expanding gas. This rapid expansion, really a drop in pressure, is accompanied by the drop in temperature which we use to cool our food.

Now we can look at the Wilson cloud chamber, a simple diagram of which is shown in figure 334. The chamber is a closed box with clear glass walls on all sides but one. This last side is movable and can be a rubber diaphragm. Inside the chamber is air that is saturated with water vapor. When the valve below is opened, the rubber wall is sucked down and the air in the chamber expands suddenly. This sudden expansion cools the air and it becomes supersaturated. It has more water vapor at this lower temperature than it can normally hold. If the chamber is dust-free, no droplets can form.

However, if we have radioactive materials in the chamber, ionizing the air with the rays they emit, droplets will form wherever there are ionized gas atoms. These droplets will mark the path of the rays. If at the same time we shine a bright light into the chamber to illuminate the water droplets we can take a photograph of the paths of the rays.

338. Cloud chamber photograph of billion-volt particles. *Protons, speeded up to an energy of 1.2 billion electron volts in a giant machine called the cosmotron, were directed against a brass target. Flying fragments from the collision penetrated 1¼ inches of steel, two heavy doors, and 195 feet of air before passing through the cloud chamber.*

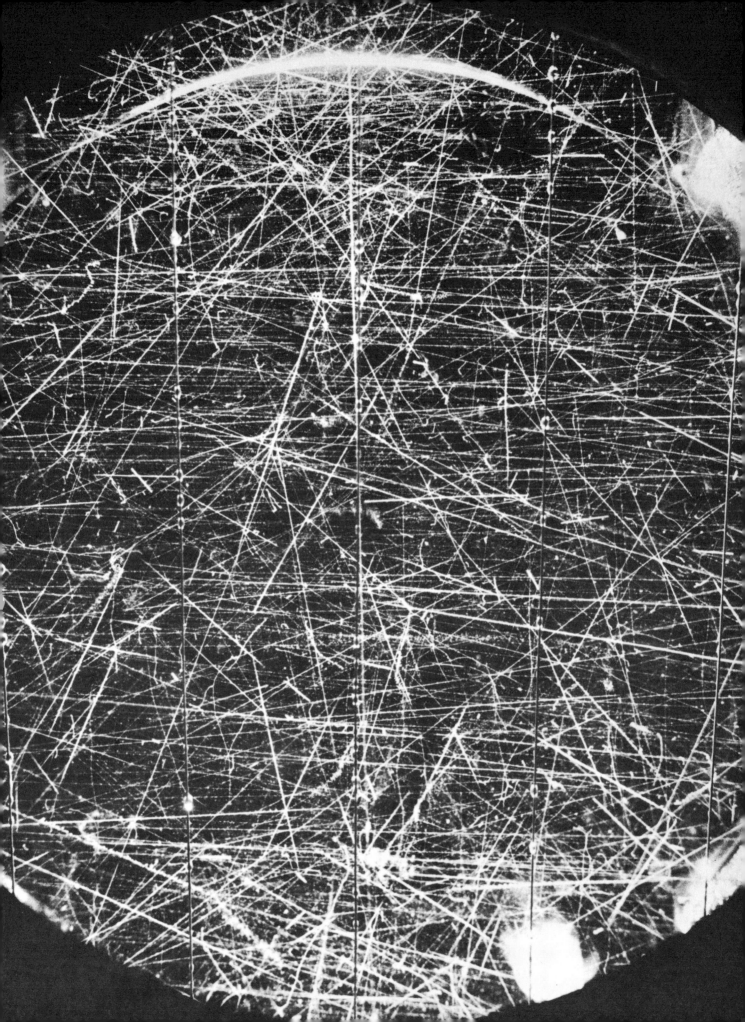

Cloud Chamber Snapshots of Alpha-, Beta-, and Gamma-Ray Tracks   In figures 335, 336, and 337 we can see such pictures taken of the tracks of alpha rays, beta rays, and gamma rays. Remember that what we are seeing are little water droplets that collected about the gas atoms ionized by the passage of the rays through the air in the chamber.

The alpha-ray tracks are heavy, straight lines stretching away from the radioactive material which is the bright patch at the bottom of the circular picture in figure 335. The lines are heavy because the alpha particles have a large mass and produce many ions, over 25,000 ions in each inch of path length. The lines are straight because the heavy alpha particles are not deflected by their collisions with the gas atoms.

The beta particles, or electrons, produce only about 250 ions per inch of travel. Their paths are thin. The paths are jagged or curved, because the lightweight electrons change direction with each collision. However, there are a few straight tracks, representing very fast electrons which were able to bully their way straight through. The beta rays in figure 337 originate in

339. Neutron-proton collision. *Three long cloud chamber streaks starting from a single point (a) betray a collision between an energetic neutron and a proton. The uncharged neutron left no trace. The struck proton (b) was hurled straight downward. Two pi mesons resulting from the collision produced the two slightly curved tracks (c) to the left of the proton. The tracks are curved oppositely in a magnetic field because one meson was positive and the other negative.*

the bright patch at the bottom which is, again, the source material.

In figure 336, we see the very different track of a beam of gamma rays which traveled from left to right across the picture. Along the center line, which represents the actual path taken by the gamma rays, electrons were knocked out of atoms by some of the gamma rays. The remaining gamma rays simply continued on, leaving no trace of their passage. The electrons, which were the casualties of the collisions that did occur, stumbled their way through the gas. The ionization produced along their straggly paths resulted in the photograph shown in figure 336.

Realization of an Old Dream   Until the year 1919, man had to be content with the role of spectator in the drama of nuclear transformations. He could place a sample of radium in a cloud chamber and interpret the photographs he took. He could learn more and more about the rays that were emitted by radioactive substances. But he could only move these substances about. He could not cause a nucleus to change itself at his command.

For ages, man dreamed of being able to convert one element into another. Alchemists spent their lives searching for magic formulas that would make gold out of cheap metals. In 1919, Lord Rutherford was the first man to accomplish such a feat. He did not change iron into gold, but he did change the gas nitrogen into the gas oxygen.

Rutherford did this by attacking the

340. Bubble chamber for detecting highly active particles. *This mammoth machine can be likened to a liquid cloud chamber. Paths of charged particles in a cloud chamber are visible because droplets are caused to condense from a supercooled vapor. Similarly, in a bubble chamber, the particles cause* superheated liquid hydrogen to vaporize, marking the trails of the particles with tiny gas bubbles. Since particles have more collisions in a dense liquid than in a thin vapor, the bubble chamber is a more sensitive instrument than the cloud chamber.

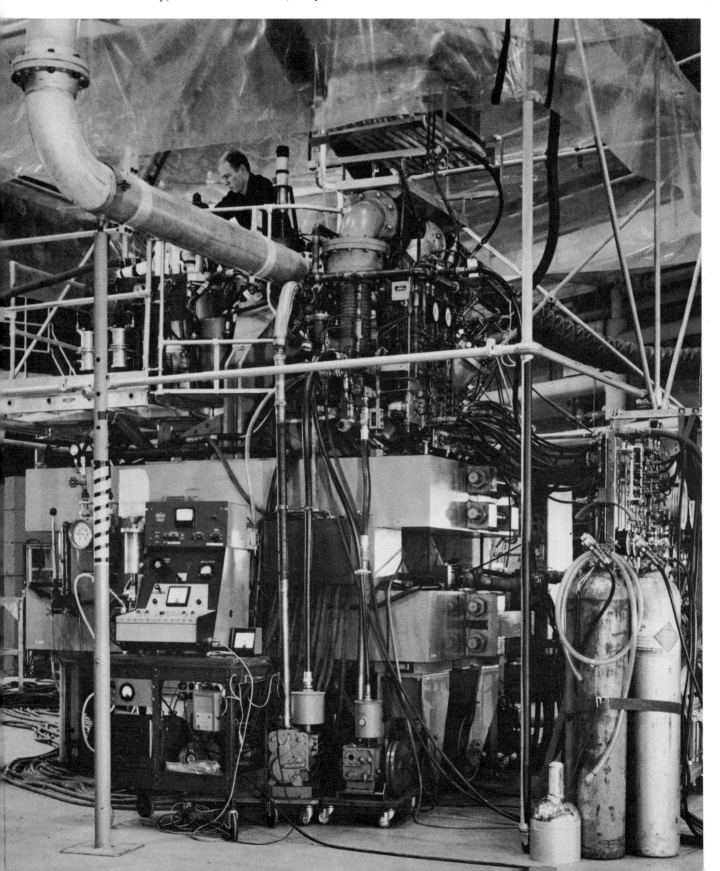

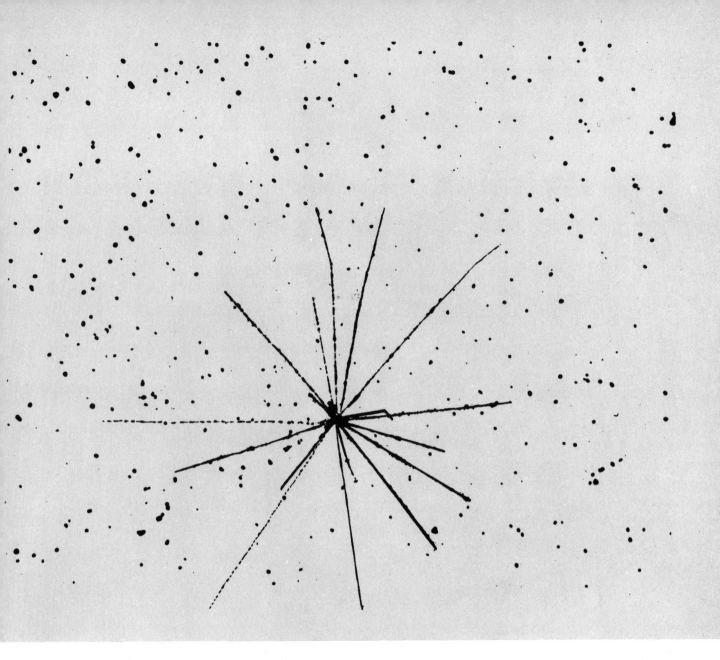

341. Atomic destruction by a 2-billion-volt particle. *The first man-made nuclear particles of 2 billion volts of energy smashed the nucleus of an atom in a photographic emulsion, resulting in this nuclear explosion. Since the incoming particle was presumably a neutron with no electric charge, it left no visible track. At least 17 distinct particles flew from the fragmented victim of the collision, leaving a porcupine of tracks as a record of the event.*

nucleus of the nitrogen atom with an appropriate weapon, a nucleus of a helium atom. We have seen that the nucleus of a helium atom is the same as an alpha particle. Rutherford's bullets were alpha particles emitted at high speeds by a radioactive substance. He could not aim an alpha particle at a nitrogen nucleus the way we might sight a rifle. He therefore used his radioactive material as a shotgun, spraying nitrogen gas with a spatter of alpha particles. Most of the alpha particles merely stripped electrons from the nitrogen atoms, ionizing them. Every once in a while, however, an alpha particle shot through the surrounding electrons straight to the nucleus at the heart of a nitrogen atom. When this rare event occurred, a strange thing happened. The alpha particle was swallowed by the nitrogen nucleus which then cast off still another particle. This new particle was found to be a proton, the nucleus of a hydrogen atom. An alpha particle entered and a proton emerged. The alpha particle added 4 units of mass and 2 units of charge to the nitrogen nucleus. The loss of the proton then subtracted 1 unit of mass and 1 unit of charge. Simple arithmetic tells us that the remaining nucleus must have been 3 units of mass heavier than the nitrogen nucleus, with 1 extra unit of charge. The nitrogen nucleus has a mass of 14 and a charge of $+7$. The new nucleus must then have had a mass of 17 and a charge of $+8$. The resulting charge of $+8$ identifies the new nucleus as that of an oxygen atom. Rutherford had changed nitrogen into oxygen.

This was indeed the realization of an old dream. Moreover, it tended to confirm earlier beliefs that the nucleus of the hydrogen atom, the proton, was one of the simple building blocks of which all nuclei are constructed. The proton has a mass of 1 and a charge of $+1$. By adding proton to proton any mass or any charge could be assembled. One additional piece was needed to make the picture complete. Let us see how this piece was found.

The Neutron Rutherford's success with the nitrogen nucleus resulted in a declaration of war against all nuclei. In laboratories throughout the world, scientists bombarded every kind of nucleus they could find with the weapons he developed. In some of these laboratories, they were looking for a very special particle to emerge from some of these battles. This particle was the *neutron*.

Several scientists, among them Rutherford himself, had predicted that there might be such a particle. This particle would have about the same mass as a proton, but it would have no electrical charge. A particle without a charge is very difficult to detect. It does not ionize atoms in its path because ionization is really a struggle between electrical charges. The neutron was said to have no charge and was given its name because of its electrical neutrality.

In 1932, James Chadwick succeeded in identifying the neutron as a particle which actually exists. The particle was produced when a nucleus of the element beryllium was hit by an alpha ray. The beryllium nucleus absorbed the alpha particle and emitted a neutron. Again we can calculate easily the result of such a reaction. The alpha particle carries in 4 units of mass and 2 of charge. The neutron has a mass of 1 like the proton, but no charge at all. Emission of the neutron therefore subtracts 1 unit of mass only. The resulting nucleus therefore has 3 units of mass and 2 units of charge more than the beryllium nucleus. It is a nucleus of carbon.

The neutron proved to have an extraordinary property which makes it still more difficult to detect. Having no charge, it is not affected by the charges in the atoms of matter through which it passes. This

342. Deuteron beam from a 60-inch cyclotron. *Deuterons are nuclei of heavy hydrogen (deuterium) and contain a proton (nucleus of ordinary hydrogen) plus a neutron. In the cyclotron they are whirled in a widening spiral, increasing in speed until they emerge with an energy that carries them many feet through the air.*

results in a lack of ionization as we mentioned before. It also leads to the conclusion that the neutron is not easily stopped by matter. The neutron penetrates matter about 10,000 times as far as an alpha particle.

The scientists were now able to place the neutron alongside the proton as the two basic components of the atomic nucleus.

What an Atomic Nucleus Is Made Of It seems logical that a nucleus is made of protons and neutrons, since protons and neutrons are sometimes emitted by a nucleus. Yet this cannot be as simple as it sounds. The nucleus also emits electrons, but we are sure that electrons cannot exist in the nucleus. A rule of physics, called by the strange name of the *uncertainty principle,* forbids the confinement of a small particle like an electron in a space as small as the nucleus. There are other reasons as well, but they are beyond the scope of our discussion.

How, then, can the nucleus emit an electron as a beta ray if the nucleus consists only of protons and neutrons? We will answer this question in a moment.

343. Cylinders of radioactive cobalt. *The five thin metal cylinders were made intensely radioactive by exposure to swarms of neutrons in a nuclear reactor. Their combined radiation is equivalent to 6000 grams of radium, six times the total amount of radium in use throughout the world in 1942. The cylinders glow through the 10 feet of water that shields them because a portion of the energy of the invisible gamma rays being emitted is converted into visible light.*

First, let us see how the protons and neutrons combine to make up the nuclei of all the different atoms.

The proton has a mass of 1 and a charge of +1. The neutron has a mass of 1 but no charge. Therefore, the mass of a nucleus may consist of both protons and neutrons, but its charge can come from protons alone. The atomic number, which is the charge on the nucleus, then tells us how many protons there are in a particular nucleus. The atomic weight tells us how many protons and neutrons there must be altogether. For example, oxygen has an atomic number of 8, that is, a nuclear charge of +8. Its nucleus must therefore have 8 protons. The atomic weight of oxygen is 16. There are 16 units of mass, 8 of which are made up of the 8 protons. Therefore, there must also be 8 neutrons. The 8 protons plus the 8 neutrons make up the total mass of 16. The charge on the 8 protons makes up the total charge of +8. A picture of the electrons, protons, and neutrons in the oxygen atom is shown in figure 320.

One more example should be enough to show the composition of a nucleus. An atom of the element aluminum has an atomic number or nuclear charge of +13. It must have 13 protons. The atomic weight of aluminum is 27. The nucleus must have a total of 27 particles of which 13 are protons. The remaining 14 must be neutrons.

Thus, the tiny nucleus is the dwelling place of the protons and neutrons whose numbers vary from element to element.

393

A Neutron Gives Birth to an Electron

Now we return to the origin of the electrons in beta rays. If electrons are emitted by a nucleus in which they do not exist, then the electrons must be created at the instant of emission. This was the reasoning of the Italian physicist, Enrico Fermi, who developed the theory concerning the emission of a beta ray from a radioactive nucleus.

Actually, protons and neutrons themselves are unstable and one is likely to change into the other. When a neutron, which has no charge, transforms into a proton, which has a charge of +1, an electron suddenly appears. The total charge must be the same before and after such a process. Before, we have only a neutron and the charge is zero. After, we must have both a plus and a minus charge so that the total is still zero. Therefore, the proton and the electron are formed together. The electron, however, cannot exist in the nucleus and therefore comes shooting out as a beta ray. In this way, an electron can be released from a nucleus in which the electron did not previously exist.

Nuclear Forces and Nuclear Energy

The miniature world of the atomic nucleus is evidently a world where strange events take place. Among the unusual features of this world are the nuclear forces that hold the protons and neutrons together. We know that such forces must exist. The protons in the nucleus all carry the same electrical charge and therefore repel each other. The protons are so close together in the nucleus that this electrical force must be very great. There must be some new, unknown force that keeps the protons from flying apart.

This mysterious, but powerful, force acts on both protons and neutrons. It appears to spring into action only when the particles are extremely close to each other. Imagine that we are pressing a group of protons closer and closer together, against the electrical force trying to drive them apart. We must press harder and harder as the particles come nearer to each other. Then, suddenly, when we reach a certain critical distance between particles, we feel the resistance vanish and the protons snap toward each other as if sucked into a vacuum. Neutrons are similarly pulled into the nucleus, but their lack of electrical charge makes them immune to the electrical force that acts to push the protons away.

Brilliant thinking and experimentation have uncovered many facts concerning the nuclear forces, but the atmosphere of mystery still lingers. In huge machines like the *cyclotron* (figure 342) and others still being built, particles like electrons and protons are accelerated to great speed and then hurled against nuclei. The scientists then examine the fragments of broken nuclei for clues to the nature of nuclear forces.

The work done by nuclear forces in bringing the protons and neutrons together is stored as energy. This is called *binding energy*. When a nucleus changes from one

kind to another, the new nucleus may not require as much binding energy as the first. The unused energy is set free. This happens, for example, when a nucleus of radium disintegrates and emits an alpha particle. The released binding energy is given to the alpha particle, permitting it to dash off at high speed. This energy is 2 million times greater than the energy obtained from burning a molecule of ordinary fuel in a furnace.

Isotopes   The new knowledge of the nucleus and atomic structure made it possible to solve an old puzzle concerning the atomic weights. When atomic weights were first measured, they seemed to be equal to or very close to whole numbers. In particular, the atomic weight of hydrogen was found to be 1.008, practically 1. This led William Prout to suggest that all atoms were made of collections of hydrogen atoms. You merely added as many

ISOTOPES OF HYDROGEN

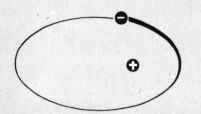

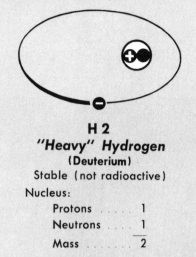

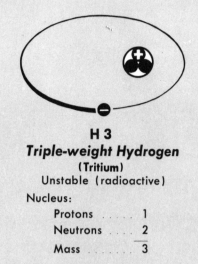

H 1
Light Hydrogen
(Protium)
Stable (not radioactive)
Nucleus:
 Protons 1
 Mass 1

H 2
"Heavy" Hydrogen
(Deuterium)
Stable (not radioactive)
Nucleus:
 Protons 1
 Neutrons 1
 Mass 2

H 3
Triple-weight Hydrogen
(Tritium)
Unstable (radioactive)
Nucleus:
 Protons 1
 Neutrons 2
 Mass 3

ISOTOPES OF CARBON

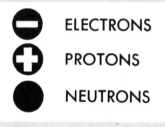

- ⊖ ELECTRONS
- ⊕ PROTONS
- ● NEUTRONS

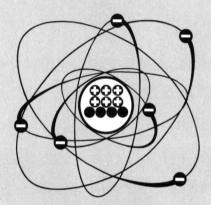

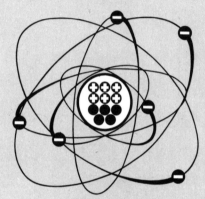

CARBON—10
Unstable (radioactive)
Nucleus:
 Protons 6
 Neutrons 4
 Mass 10

CARBON—11
Unstable (radioactive)
Nucleus:
 Protons 6
 Neutrons 5
 Mass 11

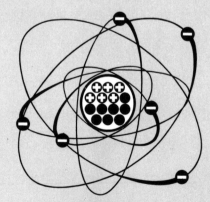

CARBON—12
Stable (not radioactive)
Nucleus:
 Protons 6
 Neutrons 6
 Mass 12

CARBON—13
Stable (not radioactive)
Nucleus:
 Protons 6
 Neutrons 7
 Mass 13

CARBON—14
Unstable (radioactive)
Nucleus:
 Protons 6
 Neutrons 8
 Mass 14

hydrogens as needed to make up the weight of any other atom. We see that this was not too far from the truth. However we now have the additional knowledge that the atomic weight is almost entirely in the nucleus, since the electrons weigh so little. We also know that there are neutrons as well as hydrogen nuclei—that is, protons. We now say that all nuclei are made up of protons and neutrons, each of which has a mass very close to 1.

It was soon discovered that many elements did not have atomic weights that were whole numbers. How is it possible to add 1 plus 1 plus 1 plus 1 and so on and reach a total which is not a whole number? Let us examine how such a situation comes about.

A chemical element is one whose atoms have the same number of electrons and the same charge on the nucleus. However, this says nothing of the neutrons. We can add or subtract neutrons from the nucleus without changing the number of protons in it, or the number of electrons circling about it. Adding neutrons to an atom does not change one element into another, but it does change the weight of the atom.

345. Isotopes of hydrogen and carbon. *The different isotopes of an element are distinguishable by the different weights of their atoms. The isotopes all bear the same chemical name because the atomic nuclei have the same electric charge carried by the positive protons ($\oplus$), surrounded by an equal number of negative electrons ($\ominus$), which causes them to behave similarly in chemical reactions. However, each isotope has a different number of neutrons ($\bigcirc$). This affects the atomic weight but not the atomic charge.*

It is possible, therefore, to have atoms of different weight belonging to the same element. Such a situation is not only possible, it was actually found to exist in nature. Since all atoms of the same element, regardless of their weight, must fall in the same place in Mendeleev's periodic table, they were given the name *isotopes*. The word isotope comes from two Greek words, *isos* meaning equal and *topos* meaning place. Isotopes are atoms having the same number of electrons and nuclear charge but different weights.

It was found that most elements do not consist of only one kind of atom but are mixtures of isotopes. There are only some 90 natural elements but there are about 290 different kinds of atoms, each atom having a different weight from the others.

Now we see why atomic weights are often not whole numbers. We find the atomic weight of an element by weighing an amount of the element and dividing by the number of atoms. Since there are atoms of different weights in the group, our answer is the average weight of all of them. Let us use chlorine as an example. Chlorine is composed of two different atoms, one with a weight of 35, the other with a weight of 37. There are two more neutrons in the second kind than in the first. If the two kinds of atoms existed in equal numbers, the average weight would be 36, midway between 35 and 37. However, chlorine is really about 75.4 per cent of the first kind of atom and 24.6 per cent of the second kind. There are more of the lighter atoms and therefore the average

346. Remote handling of radioactive materials. *A wall of lead bricks and lead-containing glass protects the operator from the dangerous radiations emitted by the material in the glass flask. Remotely controlled manipulators permit the performance of intricate and delicate experiments with safety.*

347. Transporting radioactive sources. *A plastic bottle of radioactive material is lifted from the lead container in which it is stored while being moved. Both bottle and container are clearly marked with the radiation hazard symbol. For additional safety, the radiation level is checked with a Geiger counter.*

is less than 36. The actual atomic weight of chlorine turns out to be 35.5.

Thus, the atomic weight of an element depends on how many different kinds of atoms there are of that element and how many of each kind exist. For this reason the atomic weights are usually not whole numbers.

Artificial Radioactivity Isotopes played a very significant part in the progress of modern physics, for they allowed man to create artificial radioactivity. As late as 1933, the only radioactive materials available were those which nature was kind enough to provide. In December of that year, a remarkable discovery was made by Irène Curie, the daughter of Pierre and Marie Curie, and her husband Frédéric Joliot. They bombarded some nuclei with alpha particles. Some of the nuclei were hit by the alpha particles. After the collision was over, it was found that a new nucleus had been formed, one which had never been seen before. It was an isotope of one of the known elements, an isotope not found in nature. The reason it had never been found before soon became clear. The new nucleus was unstable. In a short time, it disintegrated exactly like a naturally radioactive material. Man had created a radioactive isotope for the first time.

Here is an example of such a nuclear reaction. When a nucleus of magnesium (mass 24, charge +12) is hit by an alpha particle (mass 4, charge +2), the two combine (mass 28, charge +14) and a neutron (mass 1, charge 0) is thrown off. The loss of the neutron reduces the mass to 27, but the charge remains at +14. The element whose atoms have a nuclear charge of +14 is silicon. Thus, the new nucleus is the heart of an atom which is an isotope of silicon. In a short time, this newly created nucleus disintegrates, losing one of its charges but none of its mass. The final product is aluminum which is stable and does not disintegrate.

The discoverers of artificial radioactivity also found that some of the new nuclei emitted beta rays with a positive charge. The positive beta rays were found to be identical with the positive electrons which had recently been discovered in the course of cosmic ray research. They were given the name *positrons*.

Other physicists immediately took up the search for more radioactive isotopes. They attacked the nuclei of all the elements with alpha rays, beta rays, protons, neutrons, and even with gamma rays. The smashing of atoms became a popular sport. Many new nuclear reactions were observed. Some resulted in the transformation of one stable nucleus into another stable nucleus, as Lord Rutherford had discovered. Other reactions led to the creation of still newer radioactive isotopes which later broke apart to become stable elements, as the Joliot-Curies observed.

All of the available elements were studied down to the last one, uranium. Uranium held a surprise. Under a bombardment by neutrons, the uranium nucleus did not just change into another kind of nu-

348, 349. Physics aids biology. *A tomato plant was cut and soaked in a solution containing a radioactive form of phosphorus (radioisotope). The liquid traveled up the veins. At right is an ordinary photograph of a leaf from the plant taken with normal light. Below is an autoradiograph made by placing the leaf in contact with the film. The radioactive rays take their own picture, indicating the location of phosphorus in the plant.*

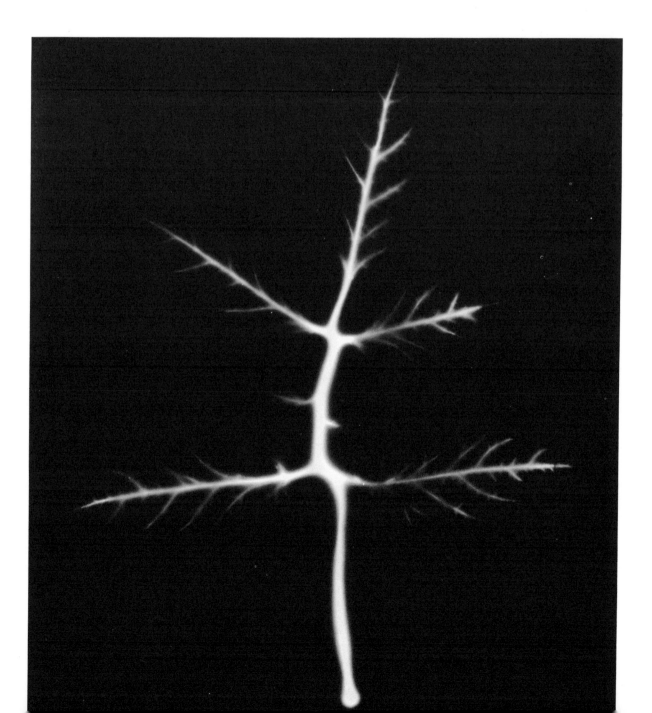

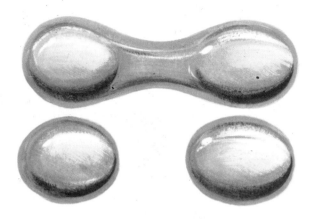

350. Liquid-drop model of the nucleus. *Niels Bohr suggested that a nucleus may resemble a drop of mercury. Surface tension holds the drop in the shape of a ball. Only a sharp blow can shatter the drop, after which it re-forms in two or more smaller balls. This may be similar to the fission of a nucleus of uranium when it is struck by a neutron.*

351. Chain reaction. *A neutron entering a mass of uranium causes fission of a single nucleus. Among the fragments are more neutrons which can go on to split more nuclei. Each fission adds to the number of neutrons, increasing the chance for further fission, until the reaction quickly spreads throughout the entire mass.*

cleus by emitting one of the usual particles. Instead it split into two heavy parts. The uranium nucleus with a charge of $+92$ simply divided into two lighter nuclei: barium with a charge of $+56$ and krypton with a charge of $+36$. The splitting was given the name *nuclear fission*.

A Drop of Liquid To Niels Bohr, the behavior of the nucleus seemed similar to the behavior of a drop of heavy liquid. Bohr was the famous Danish physicist who first described the planetary electrons in the atom. Now Bohr suggested a possible model of the nucleus. He proposed that the neutrons and the protons inside the nucleus were constantly moving about each other, like the molecules in a liquid. The motions were complicated, but the nuclear forces that attracted protons and neutrons to each other held the drop together. The picture is like that of a drop of mercury, the metal that is a silvery liquid at room temperature. When mercury spills on a table top, it does not spread out into a thin layer. Instead it breaks up into many little islands of liquid, like rain on a freshly waxed automobile, the small drops curling into tight little balls. The balling of the liquid is caused by a force called *surface tension*. Surface tension acts like a rubbery skin that pulls a liquid drop together.

Drops of mercury are fun to play with because they do not break when poked with a finger. Instead, they run away like little mice. This habit of mercury probably earned it the name of quicksilver. How-

402

ever, if a drop of mercury is hit hard and sharply, it splatters into two or more smaller drops (figure 350), each of which huddles into an even tighter little ball. Bohr suggested that this was the explanation of nuclear fission. If the nucleus is like a tight little ball of liquid it, too, will hold together unless struck violently. When a fast-moving neutron strikes the nuclear drop, the drop splits into two or more drops.

But why does this happen only with the nucleus of uranium and a few other very heavy nuclei? This is because there is a conflict in the nucleus between two opposing forces. The positive charges on the protons result in electrical forces that try to scatter the protons apart. The mysterious, only partially understood nuclear forces hold them together. The more protons there are, the greater the force trying to break the nucleus apart. For lighter nuclei, the protons are fewer in number and the electrical forces are therefore weaker. As we proceed to heavier and heavier nuclei, the number of protons increases and the electrical forces grow stronger. When we reach the nucleus of uranium, there are so many protons that the electrical force of repulsion more nearly balances the nuclear force of at-

352. Atomic explosion. *Unless the neutrons produced during a chain reaction are controlled, as in a nuclear reactor, the reaction proceeds so rapidly that it results in an awesome explosion, raising the now familiar mushroom cloud. Temperatures reach millions of degrees, approaching those inside the sun.*

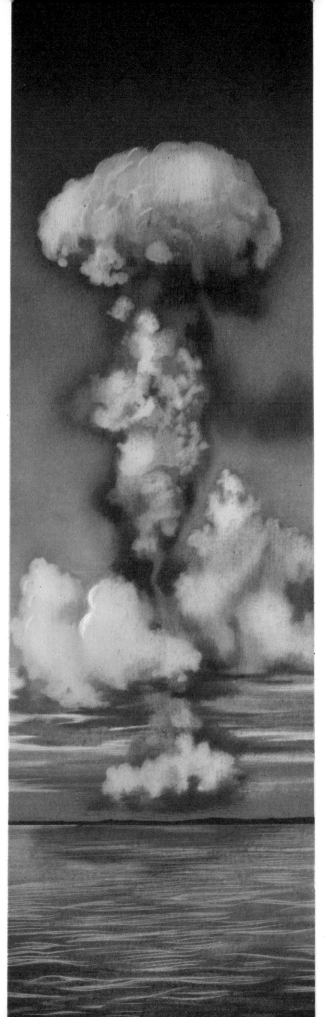

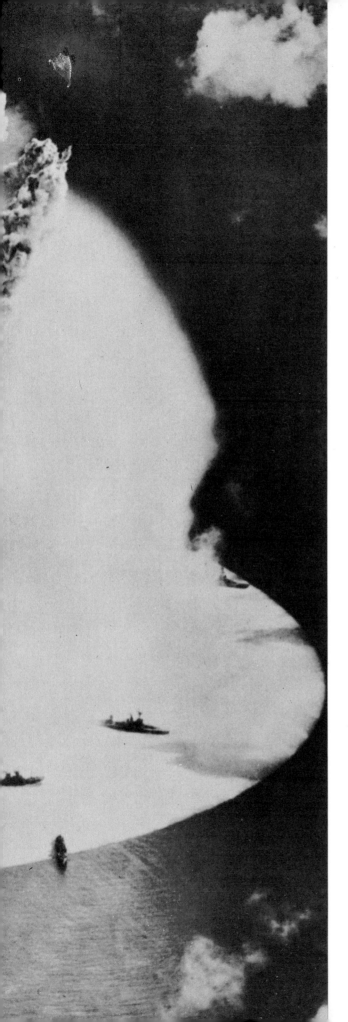

traction. The particles in the nucleus are on the verge of being pushed apart, so that the shock of a collision with a neutron is enough to upset the delicate balance and the nucleus splits.

The Chain Reaction and the Uses of Nuclear Energy

When a nucleus of uranium undergoes fission, an enormous amount of energy is released. This is energy that was formerly used to hold the nucleus together. Actually, the energy obtained when one tiny nucleus splits is very small. It is enormous only when compared to the energy obtained when a molecule of gasoline or oil is burned in the usual way. For nuclear energy to be useful, many nuclei must be split at one time.

The fission process itself provides the means for splitting many nuclei in a short time. Let us see how this happens. When the uranium nucleus splits, we get not only the nuclei of lighter elements, but also two free neutrons. These neutrons can then strike other uranium nuclei, causing them to split and release still more neutrons, as well as more energy. Thus, the more nuclei that are split, the more neutrons there are to continue the reaction. This is called a *chain reaction*. Because the neutrons are not sure to hit a nucleus, it takes a

353. Atomic bomb test. *Steam, intense heat, radioactivity, and blast pressure are intermingled in the vast bubble of energy just released during an underwater atomic bomb test. The naval vessels, tossed about like toy boats, give some measure of the forces generated by the conversion of relatively small amounts of matter into energy.*

405

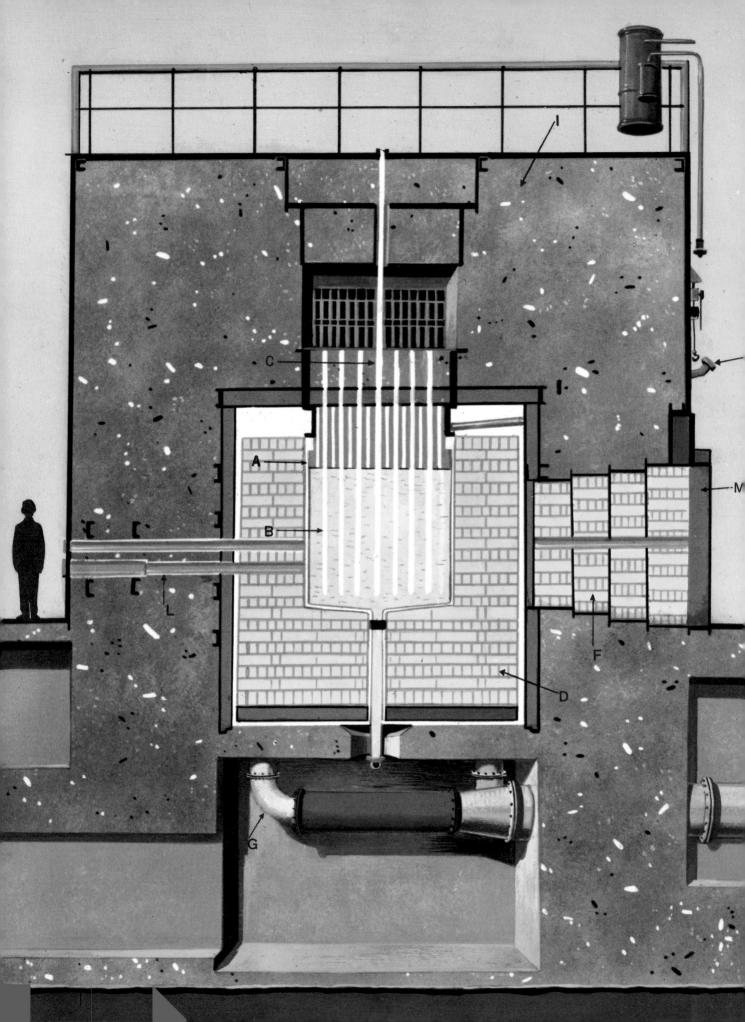

354. Interior of a nuclear reactor. *Heavy water slows down the fast neutrons produced by fission, keeping them available to continue the chain reaction. The reaction is controlled by the insertion of neutron-absorbing control rods (not shown), which remove neutrons as fast as they are produced, thus maintaining a constant level. If the control rods are inserted deeply enough, the chain reaction stops. The reactor is shut down.*

Key. A. *Tank of heavy water;* B. *Uranium bars in aluminum jackets with cooling channels;* C, L. *Tubes for conducting experiments inside the reactor;* F. *Graphite-shielded tube guiding neutrons to*

experiments outside of reactor; M. *Removable end seal for neutron tube;* D. *Graphite blocks acting as a reflector to prevent loss of neutrons;* I. *Thick concrete shield to absorb dangerous radiation;* G. *Ventilating pipe;* P. *Safety valve to release pressure if heavy water overheats.*

355. Exterior of the Brookhaven reactor. *Through some of these holes are introduced tons of pure uranium metal, the reactor fuel. Fission of the uranium produces swarms of neutrons. Other holes are used to expose substances to the neutrons, either for experimentation or for production of radioactive isotopes.*

certain amount of uranium, packed into a given space, to start a chain reaction. There must be enough uranium nuclei around to provide easy targets, as well as to set free enough extra neutrons to keep the reaction going. If we start with a small amount of uranium and keep adding more and more, we finally reach what is known as the *critical mass* and the chain reaction starts and continues. A chain reaction is shown in figure 351.

Since 1942, a tremendous amount of money and effort have been expended to make use of nuclear energy. Great technical problems had to be overcome because of the high temperatures produced and because of the dangers involved in the release of such vast quantities of energy. The scientific and engineering achievements have resulted in the ability to put nuclear energy to work.

The two great instruments that represent this development are the atomic pile and the atomic bomb. In the atomic pile (figure 354), a nuclear chain reaction is controlled so that the energy produced can be used to make electricity, heat, more radioactive materials, and other useful products. The atomic bomb is unfortunately a device of incredible destruction (figure 352) in which the chain reaction is started and permitted to run free.

In more recent years, still another nuclear reaction has been put to use in a bomb. This bomb is the hydrogen bomb and the reaction is the fusion of hydrogen. In this reaction, nuclei are not split apart. Instead, hydrogen nuclei are brought to-gether, or fused, to form a nucleus of helium. The energy in the hydrogen nuclei is greater than that needed in the helium nucleus and the unneeded energy is released. Research and experiments are now in progress in an attempt to control this reaction, so that this even greater energy may be put to constructive use. However, the fusion of hydrogen requires temperatures as high as those in the sun itself, and such temperatures melt and vaporize any material we know. The enormous problems involved in containing and controlling this reaction have not yet been solved.

Scientific knowledge and achievement have come a long way since that day in 1919 when Lord Rutherford first changed one chemical element into another. These accomplishments give us hope that further developments in nuclear physics may give man even greater control over the energy locked in the atom.

WE HAVE JOURNEYED FAR into the universe and searched the earth to find the beauties and rich variety of nature. In the end, we discover the simple harmony that ties it all together. In the universe all is matter or radiation and the two are not distinctly different but interchangeable. In matter there are protons, neutrons, and electrons. The full story is by no means this simple and probably will never be completely known. For now, we must be content with the outline.

Thus, we end this part on Matter and Energy and move on to look at Life.

Glossary

Acceleration. The time rate of change of velocity.

Alpha, beta, gamma rays. Three different types of rays emitted by radioactive substances.

Alpha ray or particle. One of the emissions of many radioactive materials, it is identical to the nucleus of the helium atom.

Anode. A positive electrode in an electrical device such as a Crookes tube or a radio tube.

Atom. The smallest particle of a chemical element that can take part in a chemical reaction without being permanently changed.

Atomic bomb. A bomb that utilizes the splitting of atoms to produce an explosion of devastating force. *See* Nuclear fission.

Atomic number. A number related to the chemical behavior of an element, used to place an element in proper order in the Periodic table. The atomic number of an element is the number of protons in the nucleus of one of its atoms. It is also the number of electrons in the atom in its neutral state. *See* Periodic table.

Atomic pile. A structure designed to sustain a chain reaction of nuclear fission through the controlled release of nuclear energy.

Atomic theory of matter. The theory that all matter is composed of small particles called "atoms," which were once considered to be indivisible into smaller particles. The atoms of one element are stated to be identical to each other but different from those of other elements.

Atomic weight. The weight of an atom of an element relative to the weight of an atom of oxygen, with the atomic weight of oxygen taken to be 16.

Avagadro's hypothesis. The theory stating that at equal temperatures and pressures, equal volumes of gases contain the same number of molecules.

Binding energy. The energy necessary to break a particular atomic nucleus into its smaller component parts.

Bohr-Sommerfield theory. The theory stating that electrons travel only in certain definite orbits about the nucleus of an atom.

Calculus. A method of analysis or calculation in higher mathematics.

Carbon. A common, black, nonmetallic element; the primary constituent of graphite, coal, and charcoal. It produces carbon dioxide when burned. A diamond is pure carbon in its crystallized form.

Cathode. A negative electrode.

Cathode ray. A stream of electrons from the cathode of a discharge tube.

Cermet. A combination material of metal and ceramic capable of withstanding extremely high temperatures. It is used for rockets and other constructions requiring tolerance to great heat.

Chain reaction. In nuclear physics, a reaction which spreads by the repetition of an initiating process. For example: the splitting of a uranium nucleus by a neutron releases more neutrons, which, in turn, cause fission in neighboring nuclei. *See* Nuclear fission.

Chemical elements. The basic or simplest components of which all substances are made. They are the simplest substances in the sense that they cannot be broken down further by chemical means.

Chlorine. A poisonous, greenish-yellow gaseous chemical element used in disinfecting and bleaching.

Cloud chamber. An enclosure containing air saturated with water vapor. When activated, it causes droplets to condense along the paths of ionizing particles, making their routes visible.

Compound.   A substance produced by the chemical union of two or more elements, such as sodium and chlorine, which combine to make salt.

Conservation of matter.   The law which states that matter cannot be created or destroyed, only transformed. It is now modified by the theory of relativity, which includes the conversion of matter into energy. *See* Theory of relativity.

Corpuscular theory of light.   The theory stating that light is composed of fast-moving corpuscles or small particles.

Critical mass.   The smallest amount of fissionable material which under the proper conditions can sustain a chain reaction.

Crookes tube.   One of the earliest forms of vacuum tube, it was invented by Sir William Crookes, who used it in his studies of electrical discharge at low pressures.

Cubic inch.   A unit of volume measurement. A cubic inch is equivalent to a volume one inch wide by one inch long by one inch deep.

Cyclotron.   An apparatus that whirls charged particles in circular paths of increasing diameter at increasingly high speeds in order to make them more effective in bombarding atomic nuclei.

Electric arc.   A visible band of electricity caused by the passage of current across an insulating gap.

Electrode.   A conducting terminal in an electrical apparatus. The positive electrode is called the anode, the negative terminal the cathode.

Electromagnetic induction.   The process by which moving magnets and electrical charges influence one another.

Electromagnetic waves.   The waves of electromagnetic radiation which travel through space at a speed of about 186,000 miles a second. These waves include ultraviolet rays, visible light rays, infrared rays, and radio waves.

Electron.   The negative elementary electric charge.

Electron shell.   Term used to describe the grouping of electrons surrounding the nucleus of an atom.

Energy.   The capacity to do mechanical work. Energy appears in many forms, such as heat, electricity, magnetism, etc., each of which can be transformed into the other. A quantity of energy is measured by the work it can perform if converted into mechanical form.

Energy level.   One of the many states in which particles of matter may exist; for example, the conditions of electrons in an atom.

Evaporation.   The escape of molecules from a liquid or a solid, forming a vapor.

Force.   The cause that is capable of changing the direction or speed of a body.

Frequency.   The number of complete cycles per second of a periodically repeated process, such as the back-and-forth flow of an alternating electric current.

Friction.   The resistance to motion occurring between two surfaces in contact with one another.

Gram.   A unit of mass or weight. There are 28.3 grams to an ounce.

Gravitation.   The force that attracts bodies toward one another by virtue of their respective mass.

Gravity.   The gravitational force of the earth which attracts objects toward the earth's center. The weight of an object is the force of gravity upon the object.

Heat.   The form of energy related to the motion of the molecule of a substance. Temperature is a measure of heat energy in a body.

Hertzian wave.   Electromagnetic radiation produced by the oscillations of electricity in a conductor. It is another name for radio waves and was named after Heinrich Hertz in 1888.

Hydrogen bomb. A bomb in which a powerful explosion is produced by nuclear fission, that is, the joining of two separate nuclei to form a single nucleus of a heavier element.

Inertia. The tendency of all objects and matter in the universe to remain motionless if motionless, or if moving to continue moving in the same direction with the same speed unless acted on by an outside force.

Ion. An atom or group of atoms that carry an electric charge. The charge is positive when such a group has fewer electrons than protons, and the charge is negative when it has more electrons than protons.

Ionization. The process of changing uncharged atoms or groups of atoms into ions.

Isotope. One of several kinds of atoms of the same element which have the same atomic number but different atomic masses. They exhibit similar chemical behavior because they have the same number of electrons and protons. Their weights are different because they do not have the same number of neutrons.

Kepler's first law. This states that the orbit of a planet is an ellipse with the sun at one focus.

Kepler's second law. This states that a line between the sun and an orbiting planet sweeps over equal areas at equal times.

Kepler's third law. This states that the squares (a square is a number multiplied by itself) of the periods (times for one complete revolution) of the planets are proportional to the cubes (a cube is the square of a number multiplied again by the number itself) of their mean distances from the sun.

Kilocycle. 1000 cycles.

Kinetic energy. A body's energy in the form of its motion.

Light. Electromagnetic waves in a range of frequencies to which our eyesight is sensitive. May also include invisible rays such as infrared and ultraviolet.

Liter. A unit of volume equivalent to slightly less than a dry quart. It is the volume of 1000 grams of water under standard conditions.

Magnetic pole. One of the two points of a magnet, just outside which the magnetic intensity is greatest.

Magnetism. The properties of force—having the power to attract—found in magnets. Also, the property of certain substances and electrical devices so that they repel or attract one another. This property is distinguished from electrical or gravitational forces in that it is not directly related to charge or mass.

Mass. The quantity of matter found in a body as represented by the gravitational force it experiences in relation to other bodies. Also, a measure of inertia: the resistance a body offers to attempts to change its motion.

Matter. Formerly defined as whatever occupies space. However, with the present knowledge of the interchangeability of mass and energy, the character of matter is no longer clearly distinct.

Microscope. An optical instrument with a lens, or combination of lenses, used to magnify small objects.

Milligram. A unit of mass or weight: one thousandth of a gram.

Minus, or negative, charge. An electrical charge which repels other minus charges but which attracts plus, or positive, charges.

Molecule. The smallest particle of a substance

still retaining its chemical identity and character.

Multiple proportions. The law stating that when elements combine to form compounds, the quantities that join together must be of specific proportions. These proportions must be expressed as ratios of simple whole numbers.

Neutron. A nuclear particle that has approximately the same mass as a proton, but no electric charge.

Nitrogen. A colorless gaseous element that comprises about 78 per cent of the earth's atmosphere.

Noble gas. One of a number of gaseous elements, that include helium and neon, known for their chemical inertness.

Nuclear fission. The splitting of the nucleus of an atom into two nuclei of lighter atoms, and other fragments, by collision with a neutron.

Orbit. The path of a planet about the sun. Also, the path of any body about a more massive body to which the former is attracted by a gravitational, electrical, or similarly acting force. For example, in the Bohr atom, the electron orbits the nucleus.

Oxygen. A colorless, odorless, gaseous element that makes up about 21 per cent of the earth's atmosphere. It combines with most other elements to form oxides.

Pauli exclusion principle. This states that no two electrons in the same atomic or molecular system can have all their quantum numbers identical.

Periodic table. A chart of the elements based on the principle that certain properties of the elements recur in regular cycles when the elements are arranged in the order of their weights or atomic numbers.

Photon. A quantum, or single bit, of light energy. In quantum theory, light has both particle and wave properties. The frequency as a wave is pro-portional to the energy in a quantum, or particle, of light. *See* Quantum theory.

Physics. The science that concerns itself with the study of energy and the properties of matter.

Plum-pudding atom. An atomic model in which the electrons are embedded throughout the mass of an atom, much like raisins in a plum pudding.

Plus, or positive, charge. An electrical charge which repels another plus charge but attracts a minus, or negative, charge.

Positive, or canal, rays. A stream of positively charged atoms or molecules attracted to the cathode of an electrical discharge tube. They were studied by causing them to flow through the cathode by way of an air hole, or "canal."

Positron. A positively charged particle with the mass of an electron and a charge equal to that of an electron, but opposite in polarity.

Potassium nitrate. A colorless, crystalline substance used as an oxidizing agent in gunpowder and explosives. Also known as saltpeter.

Potential energy. A form of mechanical energy within the particular system by virtue of the position of the latter's parts; as in a stretched spring or raised weight.

Powers of ten. A system of mathematical short-hand based on simple multiplication whereby 10 is raised to the nth power. 10^n represents one followed by n. For example, 10^4 (10 to the fourth power) is 10,000.

Pressure. Force per unit area. Gas pressure is produced by the bombardment of molecules against confining walls.

Prism. A transparent object, usually of glass, with a triangular cross section. It refracts each frequency component in sunlight differently, and fans the white light into a rainbow series of colors. *See* Spectrum; Spectroscope.

Proton. A positively charged elementary particle which is an essential component of the nucleus of an atom.

Quantum. The smallest quantity of energy which can be transferred by electromagnetic waves of a given frequency.

Quantum number. A whole number by which energy levels in an atom are specified.

Quantum theory. The theory that energy is divided into small bits called quanta. A quantum is the smallest amount of energy that can be transmitted; it has a magnitude proportional to the frequency of the radiation. The theory was introduced by Max Planck.

Radioactivity. The spontaneous emission of subatomic particles from the nuclei of certain unstable elements.

Radio waves. Electromagnetic waves with frequencies in the kilocycle (thousands of cycles per second) to megacycle (thousands of millions of cycles per second) range.

Radium. An intensely radioactive metallic element found in minute quantities in pitchblende and other uranium minerals.

Reflection. The rebounding of light rays from a surface in such a way that the angle at which the given ray is returned is equal to the angle at which it strikes the surface.

Refraction. The change in direction of a ray of light when it passes from one medium, such as air, to another, such as water. It is related to the different speeds of light in each separate medium.

Relativity. *See* Theory of relativity.

Rusting. The combining of oxygen with metal, producing a brownish-red oxide. It is most prevalent in iron and steel.

Sodium. A soft, silver-white metallic element. Salt and baking soda contain sodium.

Spectroscope. Any one of a variety of instruments used for separating the colors or frequency components in light in order to permit a study of the resulting spectrum.

Spectrum. A band of colors formed when a beam of light is broken up by passing through a prism, or by some other means. *See* Prism.

Speed. The time rate at which distance is covered by a moving body or object without reference to direction.

Stable (or inert) element. A nonradioactive element which remains unchanged, and does not disintegrate by emitting a subatomic particle.

Sulfur. A nonmetallic solid element which burns with a blue flame and stifling odor. It is used in many chemical compounds such as sulfuric acid.

Telescope. An optical instrument used to aid the eye or camera in viewing or photographing distant objects, as the heavenly bodies.

Theory of relativity. Introduced by Albert Einstein, the theory treats space and time not as separate and absolute quantities, but as interrelated and dependent on the motion of the observer. Consequences of the theory, such as the equivalence of mass with speed, and the bending of light rays by gravitation, have been successfully confirmed. The theory was a turning point in modern physics.

Ultraviolet rays. Electromagnetic radiation of wave lengths shorter than those of visible light but longer than those of x-rays. Ultraviolet rays are used for healing, forming vitamins, etc.

Uncertainty principle. The idea that pairs of properties, such as the velocity and position of a particle, cannot be known exactly at the same time: more certainty in the one increases the uncertainty in the other. The uncertainty principle is of great importance in nuclear physics: for example, it implies that an electron cannot stay in the nucleus of an atom, since if we knew its position with any great precision, its velocity would be so uncertain that it could easily have enough velocity to escape.

Uranium. A hard, heavy, white radioactive metallic element.

Vacuum. A space empty of all matter. The term is used also for almost-empty spaces and very low pressures.

Van Allen belt. Dangerous concentrations of radiation surrounding the earth in a doughnut shape, producing a hazard in space travel.

Velocity. Rate of change of position. It includes both speed and direction.

Water vapor. The evaporated molecules of water.

Wave. A periodically varying disturbance, such as light or sound, that progresses from point to point through a medium (such as air or water).

Wave length. The distance a wave travels between one point of a cycle and an identical point in the next cycle. For instance, if the cycle is peak-to-peak, the wave length is the distance between identical points on the two peaks.

Wave theory. This states that light travels in the form of waves or vibrations.

Weight. The force exerted on a body by the earth's gravity. May also be used in relation to other planets.

Weightlessness. The apparent absence of the earth's gravitational pull, such as occurs during the orbital flight of space capsules. It is a consequence of free fall and may also be felt in a runaway elevator.

X-ray. A type of electromagnetic wave of varying short wave lengths formed when a cathode ray impinges upon a solid body.

PHOTOGRAPHIC CREDITS

Air Reduction Sales Company, 312, 313, 315
Allied Chemical Corporation, 291–294, 297
Argonne National Laboratory, 282, 342, 348, 349
Courtesy Atomic Energy Commission, 353
Bell Telephone Laboratories, Incorporated, 277
The Bettmann Archive, 267, 276, 279, 317, 325
Brookhaven National Laboratory, 332, 333, 338–341, 343, 344, 346, 347, 355
Curtiss-Wright Corporation, 269
I. E. du Pont de Nemours and Company, 311
General Electric Research Laboratory, 298–303, 306
General Motors Research Laboratories, 289, 290

The Hospital for Special Surgery, New York City, 326
Courtesy of the International Nickel Company, Incorporated, 284
Photo courtesy of Narinder S. Kapany, 272, 273
Merck Sharp and Dohme Research Laboratories, 263, 307–309
New York Public Library, Picture Collection, 266, 270, 295, 318, 319, 327, 328
Olin Mathieson Chemical Corporation, 264, 281, 285
Robert Snyder and Associates, 275
United States Steel Corporation, 305
Westinghouse Research Laboratories, 286–288

Index

Index

Recent Developments

AND ADDITIONAL INFORMATION

RAPID PROGRESS has been made toward a clearer understanding of matter in its grosser, more outward aspects. Chemists, physicists, and engineers now know a great deal more about how molecules are held together, as well as the forces required to tear them apart. They have increased their knowledge of the growth of crystals, in nature or in the laboratory. They know how to study defects in seemingly perfect crystals, how to follow the movements of such flaws under applied stresses, and how to estimate the influence of the defects on material properties. These defects are missteps during the growth of the crystal—as if nature were a bricklayer with hiccups. A large amount of information has been gathered about the physical strength, the magnetic and electrical properties, and the chemical characteristics of substances and the way they change as a result of temperature, pressure, magnetic or electric fields, and exposure to radiation. New substances have been synthesized, complex compounds rivaling those made by nature have been made in the laboratory and factory.

Matter has been cooled to within a fraction of a degree of *absolute zero* (the temperature at which all motion stops, including the vibrations and turnings inside molecules). Some substances behave strangely at very low temperatures, exhibiting *superconductivity* (the apparent loss of all resistance to the flow of electrical energy). These are used in supercooled electromagnets in which enormous currents exist without excessive heating, resulting in massive magnetic fields. Substances are superpurified, then minute quantities of selected atoms are added to make useful semiconductors. *Semiconductors* are classed between electrical *insulators*, which greatly impede the flow of electricity, and *conductors,* such as copper and silver, which offer only slight opposition to the flow. The special characteristics of semiconductors are put to widest use in the *transistor*, a small, durable bit of metallic crystal which needs almost no power for its operation and which is rapidly replacing the familiar vacuum tube in electronic circuitry.

The Mood of Nineteenth-Century Physics In the latter half of the nineteenth century many scientists tended to become somewhat complacent. With the aid of Newton's Laws astronomers thought that they had conquered the stars. The atomic theory seemed to give chemists the basis for the periodic table of the elements and an insight into the chemical behavior of matter. Maxwell's equations proved that light, electricity, and magnetism were tied together and, on theoretical grounds, they derived the velocity of light, one of the fundamental quantities in nature.

It appeared to many that the future might hold only a refinement of techniques and instrumentation—the adding of more decimal places to the known quantities as more precise methods were developed.

Yet, some disturbing signs persisted. Mercury's path had a wobble that wasn't satisfactorily explained. Heat waves from hot bodies had a distribution of frequencies that was somewhat puzzling. The ether, assumed to permeate the universe, was not altogether a happy invention. Overall, however, past successes gave much cause for self-satisfaction.

This complacency was soon shattered. X-rays were discovered, then radioactivity and the electron. The quantum theory was devised to explain radiation from heated bodies. Alpha particles bouncing back from atoms disclosed the central nucleus. The Michelson-Morley experiment proved that the mysterious ether did not exist and that the velocity of light was a constant number independent of the motion of the source. The theory of relativity demonstrated the equivalence and interchangeability of mass and energy. All these struck in quick succession like a devastating artillery bombardment.

The revolution did not lose momentum. In the 1920's the quantum theory was extended by the development of *quantum mechanics* (a mathematical treatment by wave equations of the behavior of particles and rays). A particle which has mass and can travel at any speed up to nearly the speed of light and a ray which is apparently pure energy,

1

has no mass, and always travels at the speed of light could no longer be considered two separate and different entities. Both were tiny bundles of energy with a dual character. They could act as either waves or particles, one link being the relativistic formula $E = mc^2$—the energy (E) equals the product of the mass (m) times the square of the speed of light (c^2).

An example of how deeply the new theories depart from the old, classical view of nature is the *Uncertainty Principle*, or *Principle of Indeterminacy*, first stated by Werner Heisenberg, one of the founders of quantum mechanics.

Fine details of the crystal structure of silver. *This photomicrograph shows the many faults, defects, and dislocations in the crystal structure of a thin film of silver (about 100 to 200 atom layers).*

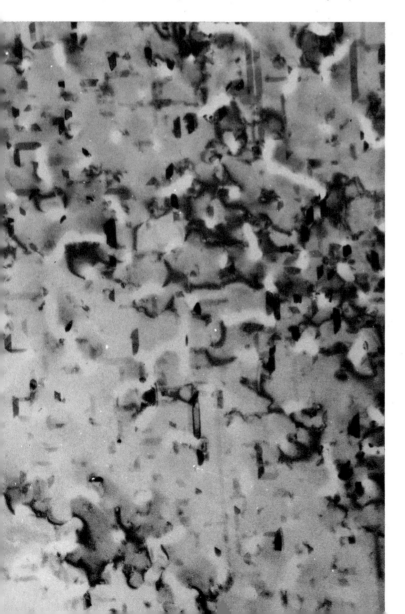

The Uncertainty Principle In classical physics it was assumed that physical quantities such as *position* (distance from some reference point) and *momentum* (velocity times the mass of the moving particle) had absolutely definite values and that there was no theoretical limit to the accuracy with which these quantities could be measured or predicted. There might be practical limits—the equipment needed might be too large or too small, too expensive or too complex, and beyond our present technical ability to construct—but there was no doubt that the quantities had perfectly precise magnitudes even though these escaped us at the moment.

In quantum mechanics this is not the case at all. The description of the position and momentum by means of a wave equation does not yield a statement such as: This is where the particle is and this is its momentum. Instead, solutions of wave equations are formulas which give a *range* of possible positions and a *range* of possible *momenta*. With these formulas one can calculate the probability that the particle lies within a particular narrow strip of space and the probability that the momentum of the particle lies between two particular values of momentum. The narrowness of the possible ranges within which the position and momentum lie depends on the physical conditions surrounding the particle, such as the energy and the forces acting on it. For a given set of conditions there may be a tiny region where the formula indicates it is most likely we will find the particle—that is, where the probability is highest. This is interpreted as being the average position of the particle. However, the particle must be considered to be free to occupy all other positions within the permissible range as well. The probability of finding it in these other locations will be less than at the average position (at some locations the probability may be very small indeed). Thus, the probability can be taken to be the fraction of the time the particle spends in some tiny region associated with that probability. Similarly, the probability that the momentum lies within some portion of the permissible range is calculated by the fraction of the time the momentum has values within those limits.

A crucial point is that the formulas for position and momentum probabilities in quantum mechanics are not independent of each other as they are in classical physics. Therefore, if we confine the particle by some combination of forces into a narrower

Meson track. *This picture was made by a meson striking a photographic emulsion placed in a balloon 10 miles above sea level in a high-altitude study of cosmic rays. The meson enters from the corner of the picture, strikes the nucleus of an atom in the emulsion, and several particles (mesons and alpha particles) shoot out in a "star."*

and narrower region, the range of possible momentum values may grow broader. This consequence is expressed as the Uncertainty Principle. It states that if we measure the position of the particle with some accuracy (A), and we measure the momentum of the particle with some accuracy (B), the product of the two errors ($A \times B$) can never be less than some small number (approximately 10^{-27} when the position is measured in centimeters, the mass in grams, and the velocity in centimeters per second).

This means that we can never, even in our imagination, eliminate all uncertainty in our knowledge of the pair of numbers representing position and momentum. The number 10^{-27} is extremely small. It is the quantity 1 divided by a number consisting of the digit 1 followed by 27 zeroes. Errors in almost all measurements are much greater than this and therefore are not in the category affected by the Uncertainty Principle. The position and momentum of a baseball, for example, can never be measured with such fine precision as to raise anxieties about the restrictions imposed by this principle.

In nuclear physics, however, where one deals with electrons, neutrons, protons, and other incredibly minute particles, and where one studies atoms and nuclei with sizes of the order of 10^{-8} and 10^{-12} centimeter, respectively, the Uncertainty Principle assumes great importance. For example, the principle demonstrates why electrons cannot reside in the nucleus. If we imagine an electron within a nuclear box with a width of 10^{-12} centimeter, we could say that we know where the electron is within an accuracy of 10^{-12} centimeter. According to the Uncertainty Principle, to localize an electron to this extent requires that its momentum can rise to $10^{-27} \div 10^{-12}$, or 10^{-15} gram-centimeter per second.

An electron at rest has a mass of about 10^{-27} gram. Its velocity is its momentum divided by its mass. In this case we cannot simply divide the momentum 10^{-15} by the mass of a nonmoving electron 10^{-27}. This would give an incorrect result implying a velocity of 10^{12} centimeters per second, which is much greater than the velocity of light (3×10^{10}, or 30 billion centimeters per second). The reason this procedure is wrong is that very small particles moving at very fast speeds no longer obey Newton's Laws but come under the jurisdiction of Einstein's *Theory of Relativity*. This theory states that the mass of a particle is relative to its velocity; specifically the mass of the electron rises as its speed increases according to the formula

$$m = m_0 \div \sqrt{\frac{1 - v^2}{c^2}}$$

where m is the relativistic mass of the electron (the mass during motion), m_0 is the mass at rest, v is the velocity of motion, and c is the speed of light. The symbol $\sqrt{}$ indicates the square root of the quantity it contains.

The higher the velocity (v), the smaller the denominator of the fraction, and therefore the greater the moving mass (m) as compared with the rest mass (m_0). It can be seen that the closer the speed (v) comes to the speed of light (c), the closer the denominator comes to zero. If the particle could actually travel at the speed of light, its mass would become infinitely large. Since this is impossible, the speed of light is the limiting speed of particles in the universe.

If the momentum of the electron imagined to be confined in the nucleus is divided by its relativistic mass, the calculated velocity of the electron is about 0.1 per cent less than the velocity of light. At such a momentum and speed the electron could not be confined by the forces in the nucleus and it would escape. It would be like a space rocket launched on earth with sufficient velocity for it to escape the forces of gravity, never to return.

In fact, if we try to find out how close to the nucleus the electron can be and still obey the Uncertainty Principle, the necessary calculations lead to a close approximation of the first electron orbit in the miniature atomic solar system.

Although the examples above are not completely accurate because certain wave effects are omitted, they are sufficiently valid to illustrate the power and significance of the Uncertainty Principle.

A similar uncertainty exists for the quantities of time and energy. If a reaction occurs in which energy is transferred during a period of time, we cannot know both the amount of energy and the time it takes to make the transfer with an exactness that exceeds the limits imposed by the Uncertainty Principle. If the energy is expressed in *ergs* and the time in seconds, the product of the two errors must again be no less than the number 10^{-27}. Within the scope of the Uncertainty Principle, the more we know of the energy the less we know of the time.

The fundamental point of the Uncertainty Principle is that inexactness is part of the very character of the particles and reactions themselves. There are no really specific values of position, momentum, energy, and time possessed by the particles and reactions, for these quantities are truly indefinite by nature. To this extent, Uncertainty is an erroneous name for the principle involved. The alternate title, Principle of Indeterminacy, is more appropriate but it is less commonly used.

The Uncertainty Principle also raises many philosophical questions. It implies that if we study matter and energy—that is, the contents of the universe—ever more closely, pursuing them deep into the foundations of all things, the trail disappears into a clouded region which we cannot enter. This is not due to a lack of penetrating scientific intelligence, for it is this very intelligence which marks the region as a zone of indeterminacy—an area where our questions cannot be answered, where definitions are blurred. Such a notion is disturbing in a world which tends to accept more and more the idea of a deterministic universe, a well-ordered machine working on simple cause and effect. Yet today, quantum mechanics urges on us the view that we cannot observe the action of cause and effect on the fundamental particles of nature down to the last, fine detail.

The debate on the consequences of quantum mechanics, relativity, and the Uncertainty Principle is still going on, as is the search for the fundamental particles of nature. In fact, the search has been so diligent and fruitful during the last decade that it has led to the dilemma referred to earlier—that so many particles have been discovered and others predicted on firm theoretical grounds, there are just too many candidates for the designation "fundamental." Because many of the new discoveries were unexpected—that is, they did not fit existing theories of matter and energy—the scientific world is in the position of waiting for a new theoretical structure to be built to accommodate the new data.

The modern phase of the hunt for the fundamental particles probably dates back to the discovery of cosmic rays, although it was not considered thus at the time.

High-energy nuclear particles. *This is what a stream of high-energy nuclear particles looks like as it emerges from a cyclotron. These 20-electron-volt deuterons (double-weight nuclei of hydrogen atoms) can be used by physicists to shatter waiting target atoms so the fragments can be studied, or by chemists to make samples of various elements radioactive.*

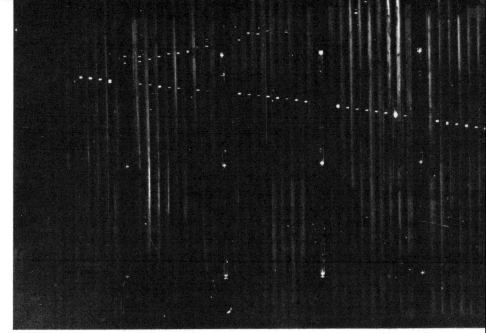

Spark chamber. *These chambers record interactions between neutrinos and other particles. The space between the plates is filled with a mixture of helium and neon gases. A charged particle passing through the chamber ionizes the gas between the plates. When 10,000 volts is applied, sparks jump between the plates along the trails of ionized gas, revealing the paths of the particles. The spark trails are then photographed, and their characteristics (such as their lengths) can be analyzed to identify the particles and their energies. At right is a photograph of a neutrino collision in a spark chamber.*

Cosmic Rays Cosmic rays were discovered early in the twentieth century during experiments in the newborn field of radioactivity. It was known that rays emitted by radioactive substances electrified the air through which they passed, making it conductive. A device called the *electroscope* was used to detect and measure the radiation.

This device is a metal box with a metal rod entering the interior through one wall. The rod is well insulated from the box itself. One end of a thin strip of gold leaf, very light in weight, is attached near the end of the rod inside the box. When the rod is electrically charged, as by momentarily connecting the terminals of a high-voltage battery between the rod and the box, the rod remains charged for some time after the battery is removed. Because the rod and the attached gold leaf both carry the same kind of electrical charge—and like charges repel one another—the gold leaf is repelled by the rod. Since the leaf is free to move at its unattached end and is very light in weight, it stands away from the rod when the charge is applied.

If the air in the box is clean and dry, the leaf remains stiffly outstretched for a long time. If radiation passes through the box, however, the electricity it produces in the air permits the charge to leak off the rod and the leaf slowly returns to its resting place against the rod. The rate at which the leaf returns is a measure of the intensity of the radiation.

It was found that the charge leaked off the rod at a faster rate than anticipated even when no radioactive source was present. Even when the box was shielded with lead, the electroscope continued to discharge. When the electroscope was taken to high mountaintops or lifted even higher by balloons, the discharge became more rapid than at sea level. It was evident that highly penetrating radiation was coming from somewhere outside the earth. This radiation was called *cosmic rays*.

Much has been discovered about cosmic rays. We know, for example, that the rays received at the earth's surface are secondary rays, produced by the collision of primary cosmic rays with the gases of the atmosphere. An average of about 10 secondary rays per minute pass through each square inch of surface. At an altitude of 10 miles the number increases to several hundreds per minute. At still higher levels and above the atmosphere, where primary cosmic rays become pronounced, the bombardment presents a hazard to space travel.

The *primary cosmic rays* are the nuclei of atoms traveling at enormous speeds for such heavy particles. Some 87 per cent are the nuclei of hydrogen atoms (protons), about 12 per cent are the nuclei of helium atoms, and the small remainder are the nuclei of heavier atoms. Their speeds are represented by energies ranging from hundreds of millions of electron volts to nearly one billion billion electron volts. It is as if in being accelerated to such speeds, the nuclei were jolted free of their surrounding electrons.

Since the primary cosmic rays carry electrical charges (their missing negative electrons leave the nuclei positive in charge), they are deflected by the earth's magnetic field. This tends to channel them toward the north and south poles. Very high energy particles can approach the earth more closely at the equator without their paths being bent by the earth's magnetism, but lower energy rays enter the atmosphere nearer the poles. As a result, the number of primary cosmic rays per square inch per minute varies from about 50 near the equator to about 200 near the poles.

The source of cosmic rays is still a matter of speculation, although it seems evident that the sun emits some of them during eruptions from its surface. Conversely, the periods of maximum activity of solar flares (about every 11 years) seem to coincide with periods of reduced cosmic-ray bombardment. This is apparently due to the matter thrown out by the sun, which acts as a barrier to the penetration of cosmic rays headed toward the earth.

Since the discovery of great magnetic fields in our galaxy, it is also considered possible that hydrogen and helium, drifting from space and ionized by any of several processes, are caught by the galactic magnetism. The swirling magnetic fields may act like gigantic slingshots, swinging the nuclei around and around for millions of years, imparting higher and higher speeds before letting them fly.

The *secondary cosmic rays* consist of fragments of atoms and nuclei together with high-energy x-rays and gamma rays. In 1936, a previously unknown particle was discovered in cosmic rays. This was the *mu meson,* with a weight about 207 times that of an electron. It was of two types: one carrying a negative charge and one a positive charge.

Two years before the discovery of the mu mesons, the Japanese physicist Hideki Yukawa predicted the existence of such particles and estimated their mass. To explain the strong nuclear force that binds protons and neutrons together in the nucleus (against the mutual electrical repulsion between protons that tries to make them fly apart), Yukawa suggested

that such strong forces would be associated with certain particles that would make their appearance if the nucleus was smashed with sufficient energy. (Cosmic rays have such energy.) However, Yukawa predicted that there would be three such particles: one with a positive charge, one with a negative charge, and one neutral. He also predicted that these particles, when free, would be readily absorbed into existing nuclei. It was he who named them mesons after the Greek word for middle.

The mu mesons had approximately the right mass, but they refused to be absorbed easily by the nuclei of atoms in the atmosphere. Also, no neutral mu meson had ever been detected.

After 10 years of unsuccessful attempts to reconcile these difficulties, it was suggested by Robert E. Marshak that there were two types of meson. Soon thereafter, the second one was discovered high in the Andes Mountains in 1947. It was called the *pi meson,* and was indeed positive, negative, and neutral and was absorbed by nuclei as Yukawa had predicted.

The explanation was that the mesons are very unstable and quickly decay into other particles. The charged pi mesons decay into mu mesons and *neutrinos.* Since the pi mesons not only decay rapidly (small fractions of a millionth of a second after they are formed), but are also absorbed by surrounding nuclei, they are more difficult to find than the mu mesons, which decay a little more slowly (2 millionths of a second) and are not so quickly absorbed. It is the pi meson which is associated with the strong nuclear force, which we will discuss presently, but the mu meson was found first.

Since then, many more particles have been found (the latest count is about 100, including some that are fairly certain to exist but have not been detected because they do not leave easily observed traces. Many of these were found in high-altitude cosmic rays. (Such high-altitude studies are now aided by improved balloons and by instrumented rockets.) Others were found by means of the giant accelerators built in recent years to speed particles up to energies of several billion electron volts (speeds approaching that of light in many cases). These high-energy particles are flung at target nuclei and the emerging debris is caught in photographic emulsions or bubble chambers, where the particles betray their existence by the damage they do. In emulsions they cause photosensitive grains to change chemically so that after development the emulsion is streaked with

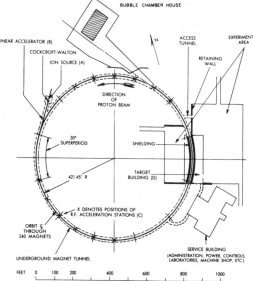

Alternating Gradient Synchrotron at Brookhaven National Laboratory. *Housed in a tunnel under 12 feet of earth is the ½-mile-circumference magnet ring of this huge proton accelerator.* At right *is a diagram of the accelerator. The proton beam is sent shooting around the magnet ring and can be led off at various points so that scientists can study it. (For example, the beam can be led off and directed to the bubble chamber, where the particles can be trapped and photographed.)*

tracks. In the bubble chamber the paths are marked by fine lines of bubbles which can be photographed under strong light. It is usually not the particles themselves which leave tracks, but rather the fragments scattered by the collisions. The instigator of the collision can be reconstructed by examination of the nature of the secondary fragments, the shape of their paths in magnetic fields, the density of ionization they create, their numbers, the lengths of their paths, and other features.

Many of the new particles behaved in such unpredicted ways that they were called "strange" and some of their properties are actually described in quantities of "strangeness." Even the mu meson, the first to be revealed, did not fit into any known scheme. The pi meson was linked to the strong nuclear force, but what part did the mu meson play?

Some of the particles are known as *antiparticles.* Antimatter is a concept which developed from quantum mechanics.

Antimatter In classical physics the notion of negative energy has no meaning. In quantum mechanics such a notion cannot be rejected, it must be interpreted. Therefore, the mathematical expression for the energy of a particle includes negative numbers.

The interpretation is based on the physical principle that a physical system always tends toward a condition of minimum energy. This is a familiar, everyday occurrence. When we raise an object away from the earth, we work against the force of gravity. This causes us to expend energy which becomes stored in the raised object. If we release the object, it falls as far as it can, yielding up the energy we put into it. The tendency toward a condition of minimum energy is illustrated therefore by a ball falling downstairs, water seeking the lowest level, and an electron finding its way to the innermost orbit around the nucleus of an atom (if this orbit has not already been filled by an early-bird electron).

In the interpretation of negative energy, say of an electron, it is presumed that electrons fall to the lowest unfilled energy level. Since negative energies are lower than positive energies, the negative energy levels are all filled. The electrons that surround us and flow in wires or circle nuclei are the electrons with positive energies because there is no room for them at lower energy levels.

However, an electron in a negative-energy state can be knocked out of its level, for example, by an interaction involving a gamma ray. This leaves a hole in the ocean of negative energy levels. Quantum mechanics indicates that this hole will have all the characteristics of an electron of positive energy but with a reserve electrical charge—positive instead of negative. But this is an apt description of a *positron*, a particle with the mass of an electron and identical to an electron in all respects, except in its possession of an opposite charge. The positron is therefore an antielectron.

The theory also predicts that a meeting of a particle with its antiparticle will result in their annihilation, their energy being totally released in the form of gamma rays. Both processes are commonly observed in nuclear physics. One, called *pair production,* occurs when a gamma ray with sufficient energy passes near a heavy nucleus (the strong nuclear influence is necessary). The gamma ray disappears and two particles are found, one an electron and the other a positron. Similarly, a collision between an electron and a positron causes the disappearance of both and the creation of gamma radiation, called *annihilation rays.* In pair production the gamma ray "kicks" a negative energy electron up to a higher level and the hole it leaves behind enters the observable world as an antielectron or positron.

Created in a like manner, there are antiprotons, antineutrons, antineutrinos, and other antiparticles, some of which have already been detected.

Consideration of the role played by some of the new particles, combined with evidence from other research, has resulted in the acceptance of a fourth force in the universe.

The Four Forces of the Universe In order of their strength, the four known forces in the universe are:

The Nuclear Force. This most powerful force is the agency that holds the atomic nucleus together. If two protons (positively charged) are brought together, the force of repulsion increases. Yet, as soon as the distance between them approaches nuclear proportions, the repulsion suddenly reverses to attraction as the short-range, nuclear force assumes control.

The Electromagnetic Force. About 100 times weaker than the nuclear force (at a given distance), this is the familiar force which acts on electrical charges. Since magnetism is attributable to the spinning of electrons in atoms, and since magnetism and electricity are so interrelated, electricity and magnetism are considered as one general concept labeled *electromagnetism.*

The Weak Force. This force is about 100 million million times weaker than the nuclear force. It is known only for its influence on the decay of some radioactive materials and the disintegration of some of the new particles. It also acts only at very short range like the nuclear force.

Gravitation. The last and weakest of the known forces, extremely weak even compared with the Weak Force, is still strong enough to hold the solar system together. It can act powerfully because its strength is proportional to the masses of the attracting bodies. When the bodies are as large as the sun and the planets, the forces are great. When the bodies are as small as protons or mesons, the force is not even measurable.

This question now remains: What are the fundamental particles in the construction of our universe?

Fundamental Particles Of the large number of subnuclear or "elementary" particles that have been detected or predicted, about 50 are in the class of *strongly interacting particles.* This means that they are influenced by the Nuclear Force, the strongest of the four forces known in nature. It is in dealing with these strongly interacting particles that some success has apparently been achieved by physicists in recent months. In fact, many scientists feel that matters have reached a climax and that some solution to the confusion may be at hand.

A number of theories have contributed to this feeling of imminent victory. They are schemes for arranging the particles in families so that the characteristics of the particles of a given family can be treated mathematically in such a manner that their family resemblances become evident. One such scheme is called the *SU(3) theory,* or the "eightfold way." Another more recent theory, in some ways an extension of the SU(3), is called the *SU(6) theory.* The SU(3) is so named because its mathematical approach considers all particles as composites of three fundamental particles. One of the originators of this theory, Murray Gell-Mann, has named these imagined particles *quarks.* In the SU(6) theory each of the particles in SU(3) is considered to have two possible states, making six fundamental units.

The workings of these theories cannot be stated easily. They all strongly imply, however, that our ideas of matter and energy on the level of subnuclear particles are due for a substantial overhaul. As to the question, which are the really fundamental particles, the answer may well prove to be that none is more fundamental than the next. The quarks may be only mathematical groupings rather than observable particles. As the physicist Geoffrey Chew remarked, "If there is no need for aristocracy among strongly interacting particles, may there not be democracy?"

Photographic Credits—Brookhaven National Laboratory, pages 3, 4, 5, 7; General Electric: Metallurgy and Ceramics Research, page 2